New wave
English
in practice

Daily practice workbook

Name:

www.prim-ed.com

New wave English in practice *(1st Class)*

Published by Prim-Ed Publishing 2014
2nd edition 2014
Reprinted 2016
Copyright© by R.I.C. Publications® 2014
ISBN 978-1-84654-728-7
6220IRE

Titles available in this series:
New wave English in practice *(1st Class)*
New wave English in practice *(2nd Class)*
New wave English in practice *(3rd Class)*
New wave English in practice *(4th Class)*
New wave English in practice *(5th Class)*
New wave English in practice *(6th Class)*
New wave English in practice teachers guide for classes 1–6

**NOBODY DESERVES TO BE BULLIED.
TELL AN ADULT YOU CAN TRUST.**

This anti-bullying campaign is supported by the Irish Educational Publishers' Association.

Prim-Ed Publishing
Marshmeadows
New Ross
Co. Wexford
Ireland
email: sales@prim-ed.com
web: www.prim-ed.com

Foreword

In this daily practice workbook you will be able to develop your ability to use English. Each day, you will have questions to answer in the areas of spelling, word study, punctuation and grammar. The 150 days of questions are broken into
15 units of 10 days. Each unit has a focus, which will help to improve your English skills as well as your knowledge about how language works.

At the completion of each set of 10 days, you will have the opportunity to test what you learnt by doing some revision questions.

Your daily scores are recorded in the bubble at the bottom of each day. These daily scores can be transferred onto the pupil record sheets at the front of your book. This will give an overview of your performance for the whole school year.

Be sure to read each question carefully before you answer it. If you find a question too difficult, move on to the next one. If you have time at the end, you can go back to the one you haven't done.

Contents

Pupil record sheet

Unit 1		Unit 2		Unit 3		Unit 4	
Date		Date		Date		Date	
Day 1	Day 6	Day 11	Day 16	Day 21	Day 26	Day 31	Day 36
Day 2	Day 7	Day 12	Day 17	Day 22	Day 27	Day 32	Day 37
Day 3	Day 8	Day 13	Day 18	Day 23	Day 28	Day 33	Day 38
Day 4	Day 9	Day 14	Day 19	Day 24	Day 29	Day 34	Day 39
Day 5	Day 10	Day 15	Day 20	Day 25	Day 30	Day 35	Day 40
Revision		Revision		Revision		Revision	

Unit 5		Unit 6		Unit 7		Unit 8	
Date		Date		Date		Date	
Day 41	Day 46	Day 51	Day 56	Day 61	Day 66	Day 71	Day 76
Day 42	Day 47	Day 52	Day 57	Day 62	Day 67	Day 72	Day 77
Day 43	Day 48	Day 53	Day 58	Day 63	Day 68	Day 73	Day 78
Day 44	Day 49	Day 54	Day 59	Day 64	Day 69	Day 74	Day 79
Day 45	Day 50	Day 55	Day 60	Day 65	Day 70	Day 75	Day 80
Revision		Revision		Revision		Revision	

Pupil record sheet

Unit 9

Date		
Day 81	Day 86	
Day 82	Day 87	
Day 83	Day 88	
Day 84	Day 89	
Day 85	Day 90	
Revision		

Unit 10

Date		
Day 91	Day 96	
Day 92	Day 97	
Day 93	Day 98	
Day 94	Day 99	
Day 95	Day 100	
Revision		

Unit 11

Date		
Day 101	Day 106	
Day 102	Day 107	
Day 103	Day 108	
Day 104	Day 109	
Day 105	Day 110	
Revision		

Unit 12

Date		
Day 111	Day 116	
Day 112	Day 117	
Day 113	Day 118	
Day 114	Day 119	
Day 115	Day 120	
Revision		

Unit 13

Date		
Day 121	Day 126	
Day 122	Day 127	
Day 123	Day 128	
Day 124	Day 129	
Day 125	Day 130	
Revision		

Unit 14

Date		
Day 131	Day 136	
Day 132	Day 137	
Day 133	Day 138	
Day 134	Day 139	
Day 135	Day 140	
Revision		

Unit 15

Date		
Day 141	Day 146	
Day 142	Day 147	
Day 143	Day 148	
Day 144	Day 149	
Day 145	Day 150	
Revision		

DAY 1

1. What letter comes next?

   c   d   e   f   ☐

2. What capital letter goes with **g**?

   C   Q   G   O | **g** | |

3. What comes next?
   Monday …

   ◯ Tuesday   ◯ Friday

4. Which word is correct?

   ◯ funny   ◯ funne

5. Circle the word that begins with **p**.

   fly   put   is   me

6. Circle the word that rhymes with **tree**.

   friend   me   has   to

7. Write in **a** or **i**.

   c___p

8. Add **s** to mean more than one **fan**.

   ☐

9. Add **es** to mean more than one **bus**.

   ☐

10. Tick what is missing from the sentence.

    dad met Mum on the bus.

    ◯ capital letter   ◯ full stop

MY SCORE

DAY 2

1. What letter comes next?

   l   m   n   o   ☐

2. What capital letter goes with **p**?

   D   B   P   C | **p** | |

3. What comes next?
   Tuesday …

   ◯ Saturday   ◯ Wednesday

4. Which word is correct?

   ◯ sunne   ◯ sunny

5. Circle the word that begins with **f**.

   was   here   you   fly

6. Circle the word that rhymes with **got**.

   I   hot   pin   hug

7. Write in **e** or **i**.

   d___g

8. Add **s** to mean more than one **rug**.

   ☐

9. Add **es** to mean more than one **box**.

   ☐

10. Tick what is missing from the sentence.

    mum is funny.

    ◯ capital letter   ◯ full stop

MY SCORE

DAY 3

1. What letter comes next?

   i   j   k   l   ☐

2. What capital letter goes with **m**?

   N   H   E   M | **m** | |

3. What comes next?
   Wednesday …

   ◯ Tuesday   ◯ Thursday

4. Which word is correct?

   ◯ monee   ◯ money

5. Circle the word that begins with **c**.

   cut   the   house   pan

6. Circle the word that rhymes with ***bend***.

   big   no   by   send

7. Write in **a** or **i**.

   p__g

8. Add **s** to mean more than one ***pet***.

   | |
   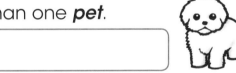

9. Add ***es*** to mean more than one ***fox***.

   | |

10. Tick what is missing from the sentence.

    ten men had food.

    ◯ capital letter   ◯ full stop

DAY 4

1. What letter comes next?

   e   f   g   h   ☐

2. What capital letter goes with **i**?

   I   L   T   O | **i** | |

3. What comes next?
   Thursday …

   ◯ Friday   ◯ Monday

4. Which word is correct?

   ◯ windy   ◯ windee

5. Circle the word that begins with **h**.

   do   can   his   nut

6. Circle the word that rhymes with ***bus***.

   by   see   fuss   look

7. Write in **a** or **i**.

   m__n

8. Add **s** to mean more than one ***pin***.

   | |

9. Add ***es*** to mean more than one ***hiss***.

   | |

10. Tick what is missing from the sentence.

    we are at school.

    ◯ capital letter   ◯ full stop

DAY 5

1. What letter comes next?

   r   s   t   u   ☐

2. What capital letter goes with **v**?

   M   B   V   W   ┌───┬───┐ v ┌───┐

3. What comes next?
   Friday …

   ☐ Wednesday   ☐ Saturday

4. Which word is correct?

   ☐ monkey   ☐ monkee

5. Circle the word that begins with **g**.

   bug   be   go   bin

6. Circle the word that rhymes with **by**.

   bus   cry   yes   mug

7. Write in **a** or **i**.

   r__b

8. Add **s** to mean more than one **cot**.

   ┌─────────────────┐
   │   │
   └─────────────────┘

9. Add **es** to mean more than one **kiss**.

   ┌─────────────────┐
   │   │
   └─────────────────┘

10. Tick what is missing from the sentence.

    he is my friend.

    ☐ capital letter   ☐ full stop

MY SCORE

DAY 6

1. What letter comes next?

   a   b   c   d   ☐

2. What capital letter goes with **e**?

   I   E   L   D   ┌───┬───┐ e ┌───┐

3. What comes next?
   Saturday …

   ☐ Sunday   ☐ Monday

4. Which word is correct?

   ☐ yollow   ☐ yellow

5. Circle the word that begins with **d**.

   bed   of   do   time

6. Circle the word that rhymes with **zoo.**

   two   one   buzz   bug

7. Write in **a** or **e**.

   f__n

8. Add **s** to mean more than one **dog**.

   ┌─────────────────┐
   │   │
   └─────────────────┘

9. Add **es** to mean more than one **boss**.

   ┌─────────────────┐
   │   │
   └─────────────────┘

10. Tick what is missing from the sentence.

    she is one today.

    ☐ capital letter   ☐ full stop

MY SCORE

DAY 7

1. What letter comes next?

   h   i   j   k   ☐

2. What capital letter goes with *t*?

   L   T   I   A | *t* | |

3. What comes next?
   Sunday …

   ☐ Saturday   ☐ Monday

4. Which word is correct?

   ☐ first   ☐ furst

5. Circle the word that begins with *m*.

   some   nut   me   hug

6. Circle the word that rhymes with *go*.

   off   done   so   up

7. Write in *a* or *e*.

   g___t

8. Add *s* to mean more than one *nut.*

   ☐

9. Add *es* to mean more than one *gas*.

   ☐

10. Tick what is missing from the sentence.

    my pet is a dog.

    ☐ capital letter   ☐ full stop

MY SCORE

DAY 8

1. What letter comes next?

   o   p   q   r   ☐

2. What capital letter goes with *a*?

   E   M   W   A | *a* | |

3. What comes next?
   Wednesday …

   ☐ Thursday   ☐ Friday

4. Which word is correct?

   ☐ litlle   ☐ little

5. Circle the word that begins with *b*.

   tub   bird   are   he

6. Circle the word that rhymes with *look*.

   log   kit   book   see

7. Write in *a* or *e*.

   h___n

8. Add *s* to mean more than one *bed*.

   ☐

9. Add *es* to mean more than one *buzz*.

   ☐

10. Tick what is missing from the sentence.

    all the bugs are green.

    ☐ capital letter   ☐ full stop

MY SCORE

DAY 9

1. What letter comes next?

   p   q   r   s   ☐

2. What capital letter goes with **s**?

   X   S   C   G | s | |

3. What comes next?
   Tuesday …

   ○ Monday   ○ Wednesday

4. Which word is correct?

   ○ pretty   ○ prettee

5. Circle the word that begins with **w**.

   two   where   cow   got

6. Circle the word that rhymes with **fan**.

   net   vet   man   to

7. Write in **a** or **e**.

   c__t

8. Add **s** to mean more than one **fin**.

   ☐

9. Add **es** to mean more than one **wish**.

   ☐

10. Tick what is missing from the sentence.

    the vet made my dog well.

    ○ capital letter   ○ full stop

MY SCORE

DAY 10

1. What letter comes next?

   k   l   m   n   ☐

2. What capital letter goes with **t**?

   D   I   T   L | t | |

3. What comes next?
   Friday …

   ○ Thursday   ○ Saturday

4. Which word is correct?

   ○ onder   ○ under

5. Circle the word that begins with **r**.

   come   ran   a   for

6. Circle the word that rhymes with **nut**.

   Dad   win   tin   hut

7. Write in **a** or **e**.

   y__s

8. Add **s** to mean more than one **net**.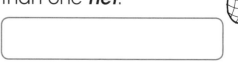

   ☐

9. Add **es** to mean more than one **dish**.

   ☐

10. Tick what is missing from the sentence.

    the old man was sad.

    ○ capital letter   ○ full stop

MY SCORE

DAY 11

1. What letter comes first?

   [ ]   b   c   d   e

2. What small letter goes with **O**?

   c   o   e   y | O | |

3. Which word is correct?

   ○ sed   ○ said

4. How many syllables in **garden**?   [ ]

5. Change **p** in **pin** to **w** to make a new word.

   [   ]

6. Write **Thirsday** correctly.

   [   ]

7. Add **ed** to **hand** to make a new word.

   [   ]

8. Add **ing** to **see** to make a new word.

   [   ]

9. Write in **e** or **u**.

   w__t

10. Tick what is missing from the sentence.

    I like your house

    ○ question mark   ○ full stop

DAY 12

1. What letter comes first?

   [ ]   c   d   e   f

2. What small letter goes with **B**?

   d   b   p   i | B | |

3. Which word is correct?

   ○ agen   ○ again

4. How many syllables in **puppy**?   [ ]

5. Change **f** in **fish** to **d** to make a new word.

   [   ]

6. Write **Satuday** correctly.

   [   ]

7. Add **ed** to **need** to make a new word.

   [   ]

8. Add **ing** to **fly** to make a new word.

   [   ]

9. Write in **e** or **i**.

   f__n

10. Tick what is missing from the sentence.

    The girl is at school

    ○ question mark   ○ full stop

DAY 13

1. What letter comes first?

   [ ]   g   h   i   j

2. What small letter goes with **F**?

   g   e   f   t   [F |]

3. Which word is correct?

   ◯ brown   ◯ broon

4. How many syllables in **teacher**? [ ]

5. Change **c** in **cot** to **p** to make a new word.

   [   ]

6. Write **Munday** correctly.

   [   ]

7. Add **ed** to **boot** to make a new word.

   [   ]

8. Add **ing** to **cry** to make a new word.

   [   ]

9. Write in **e** or **i**.

   v__t

10. Circle what is missing from the sentence.

    They will come to our house

    .   ?

DAY 14

1. What letter comes first?

   [ ]   o   p   q   r

2. What small letter goes with **N**?

   m   n   k   z   [N |]

3. Which word is correct?

   ◯ whiat   ◯ white

4. How many syllables in **ball**? [ ]
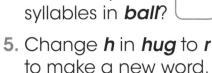

5. Change **h** in **hug** to **r** to make a new word.

   [   ]

6. Write **Teusday** correctly.

   [   ]

7. Add **ed** to **land** to make a new word.

   [   ]

8. Add **ing** to **meet** to make a new word.

   [   ]

9. Write in **e** or **i**.

   z__p

10. Circle what is missing from the sentence.

    He was next to the tree

    .   ?

DAY 15

1. What letter comes first?

   [ ]   d   e   f   g

2. What small letter goes with **C**?

   s   e   o   c | **C** | |

3. Which word is correct?

   ◯ please   ◯ pleeze

4. How many syllables in **doctor**? [ ]

5. Change **j** in **jug** to **r** to make a new word.

   [   ]

6. Write **Munnday** correctly.

   [   ]

7. Add **ed** to **end** to make a new word.

   [   ]

8. Add **ing** to **feed** to make a new word.

   [   ]

9. Write in **e** or **i**.

   l___g

10. Circle what is missing from the sentence.

    She has to go to the park

    .   ?

MY SCORE

DAY 16

1. What letter comes first?

   [ ]   v   w   x   y

2. What small letter goes with **U**?

   u   n   y   l | **U** | |

3. Which word is correct?

   ◯ witt   ◯ with

4. How many syllables in **Saturday**? [ ]

5. Change **d** in **dig** to **b** to make a new word.

   [   ]

6. Write **Wendsday** correctly.

   [   ]

7. Add **ed** to **call** to make a new word.

   [   ]

8. Add **ing** to **dry** to make a new word.

   [   ]

9. Write in **o** or **u**.

   d___t

10. Circle what is missing from the sentence.

    He put the net in the sea

    .   ?

MY SCORE

DAY 17

1. What letter comes first?

   [ ]   e   f   g   h

2. What small letter goes with **D**?

   b   d   c   e | D | |

3. Which word is correct?

   ◯ could   ◯ cudd

4. How many syllables in **hungry**? [ ]

5. Change **m** in **meet** to **f** to make a new word.

   [   ]

6. Write **Fryday** correctly.

   [   ]

7. Add **ed** to **look** to make a new word.

   [   ]

8. Add **ing** to **land** to make a new word.

   [   ]

9. Write in **o** or **u**.

   m__d

10. Tick what is missing from the sentence.

    I want to go there

    ◯ question mark   ◯ full stop

MY SCORE

DAY 18

1. What letter comes first?

   [ ]   l   m   n   o

2. What small letter goes with **K**?

   k   h   r   v | K | |

3. Which word is correct?

   ◯ every   ◯ evvery

4. How many syllables in **September**? [ ]

5. Change **b** in **bee** to **s** to make a new word.

   [   ]

6. Write **Sonday** correctly.

   [   ]

7. Add **ed** to **cook** to make a new word.

   [   ]

8. Add **ing** to **send** to make a new word.

   [   ]

9. Write in **o** or **u**.

   f__x

10. Tick what is missing from the sentence.

    We love to do art at school

    ◯ question mark   ◯ full stop

MY SCORE

DAY 19

1. What letter comes first?

   ☐ y z

2. What small letter goes with **X**?

   k   x   w   n | X | |

3. Which word is correct?

   ☐ freend   ☐ friend

4. How many syllables in **bone**? ☐

5. Change **w** in **wet** to **v** to make a new word.

   | |

6. Write **Thersday** correctly.

   | |

7. Add **ed** to **book** to make a new word.

   | |

8. Add **ing** to **look** to make a new word.

   | |

9. Write in **o** or **u**.

   g__m

10. Tick what is missing from the sentence.

    Mum said to come home

    ☐ question mark   ☐ full stop

MY SCORE ○

DAY 20

1. What letter comes first?

   ☐ h   i   j   k

2. What small letter goes with **G**?

   p   g   c   d | G | |

3. Which word is correct?

   ☐ wen   ☐ when

4. How many syllables in **hand**? ☐

5. Change **r** in **ran** to **m** to make a new word.

   | |

6. Write **Saterday** correctly.

   | |

7. Add **ed** to **sort** to make a new word.

   | |

8. Add **ing** to **cook** to make a new word.

   | |

9. Write in **o** or **u**.

   h__p

10. Tick what is missing from the sentence.

    Here are his books

    ☐ question mark   ☐ full stop

MY SCORE ○

DAY 21

1. What letter is missing?

u v ☐ x y

2. Which capital letter goes with **w**?

M R U W [**w** |]

3. Today is

[ ] .

4. How many syllables in **faster**? ☐

5. Circle the word that ends with **g**.

bag been girl of

6. Circle the odd one out.

winter hospital summer

7. Add **er** to **deep** to make a new word.

[ ]

8. Add **est** to **deep** to make a new word.

[ ]

9. Circle the word that needs a capital letter.

Her name is jill.

10. Write the number that shows where the full stop goes. ☐

He was at home

1 2 3 4

MY SCORE

DAY 22

1. What letter is missing?

p q ☐ s t

2. Which capital letter goes with **r**?

R A B K [**r** |]

3. Yesterday was

[ ] .

4. How many syllables in **sister**? ☐

5. Circle the word that ends with **n**.

once garden need all

6. Circle the odd one out.

hen robin door

7. Add **er** to **sweet** to make a new word.

[ ]

8. Add **est** to **sweet** to make a new word.

[ ]

9. Circle the word that needs a capital letter.

My sister's name is emma.

10. Write the number that shows where the full stop goes. ☐

We can ask him

1 2 3 4

MY SCORE

DAY 23

1. What letter is missing?

   a   b   ☐   d   e

2. Which capital letter goes with **z**?

   S   I   Z   X | **z** | |

3. Tomorrow will be

   _____ .

4. How many syllables in **table**? ☐

5. Circle the word that ends with **z**.

   today   best   lump   buzz

6. Circle the odd one out.

   jug   apple   banana

7. Add **er** to **small** to make a new word.

   _____

8. Add **est** to **small** to make a new word.

   _____

9. Circle the word that needs a capital letter.

   He is bigger than sam.

10. Write the number that shows where the full stop goes. ☐

    They were not there
        1   4   3   2

MY SCORE

DAY 24

1. What letter is missing?

   v   w   x   ☐   z

2. Which capital letter goes with **y**?

   K   W   C   Y | **y** | |

3. Today is

   _____ .

4. How many syllables in **teach**? ☐

5. Circle the word that ends with **s**.

   bus   sail   here   she

6. Circle the odd one out.

   pen   book   pencil

7. Add **er** to **tall** to make a new word.

   _____

8. Add **est** to **tall** to make a new word.

   _____

9. Circle the word that needs a capital letter.

   Our vet is named ben.

10. Write the number that tells where the full stop goes. ☐

    My friend is funny
        1   4 2   3

MY SCORE

UNIT 3

DAY 25

1. What letter is missing?

   h i ☐ k l

2. Which capital letter goes with *j*?

   I G J A | *j* | |

3. Tomorrow will be

   ☐ .

4. How many syllables in **going**? ☐

5. Circle the word that ends with *t*.

   ten   so   boot   push

6. Circle the odd one out.

   moon   stars   leg

7. Add **er** to **cool** to make a new word.

   ☐

8. Add **est** to **cool** to make a new word.

   ☐

9. Circle the word that needs a capital letter.

   Dad gave skip a bone.

10. Write the number which shows where the full stop goes. ☐

    Mum made a cake
    1   2   3   4

DAY 26

1. What letter is missing?

   f g ☐ i j

2. Which capital letter goes with *h*?

   K N Z H | *h* | |

3. Yesterday was

   ☐ .

4. How many syllables in **sang**? ☐

5. Circle the word that ends with *p*.

   pot   his   says   top

6. Circle the odd one out.

   bed   kettle   pillow

7. Add **er** to **warm** to make a new word.

   ☐

8. Add **est** to **warm** to make a new word.

   ☐

9. Circle the word that needs a capital letter.

   Today is monday.

10. Write the number which shows where the full stop goes. ☐

    You said hello
       2   3   1

DAY 27

1. What letter is missing?

   a   b   ☐   d   e

2. Which capital letter goes with **a**?

   O   A   Q   C | a | |

3. Today is

   _____ .

4. How many syllables in **clay?** ☐

5. Circle the word that ends with **f.**

   foot   you   off   me

6. Circle the odd one out.

   teacher   table   doctor

7. Add **er** to **rich** to make a new word.

   _____

8. Add **est** to **rich** to make a new word.

   _____

9. Circle the word that needs a capital letter.

   Today is tuesday.

10. Write the number which shows where the full stop goes. ☐

   The baby was one

     3   4   1   2

MY SCORE

DAY 28

1. What letter is missing?

   c   d   ☐   f   g

2. Which capital letter goes with **e**?

   Y   G   F   E | e | |

3. In two days it will be

   _____ .

4. How many syllables in **girl**? ☐

5. Circle the word that ends with **d**.

   bend   done   no   be

6. Circle the odd one out.

   red   yellow   dish   white

7. Add **er** to **soft** to make a new word.

   _____

8. Add **est** to **soft** to make a new word.

   _____

9. Circle the word that needs a capital letter.

   Today is wednesday.

10. Write the number which shows where the full stop goes. ☐

   We were lost

     1   2   3

MY SCORE

DAY 29

1. What letter is missing?

   g   h   ☐   j   k

2. Which capital letter goes with *i*?

   Y   I   L   M | *i* | |

3. Yesterday was

   ☐ .

4. How many syllables in **boat**? ☐

5. Circle the word that ends with **m**.

   some   my   by   room

6. Circle the odd one out.

   doctor   make   bake   cake

7. Add **er** to **old** to make a new word.

   ☐

8. Add **est** to **old** to make a new word.

   ☐

9. Circle the word that needs a capital letter.

   Yesterday was thursday.

10. Write the number which shows where the full stop goes. ☐

    Here is my school
      2   3   4   1

DAY 30

1. What letter is missing?

   m   n   ☐   p   q

2. Which capital letter goes with *o*?

   Q   C   O   S | *o* | |

3. Two days ago was

   ☐ .

4. How many syllables in **does**? ☐

5. Circle the word that ends with **b**.

   band   cub   do   pull

6. Circle the odd one out.

   chair   sweets   stool   sofa

7. Add **er** to **cold** to make a new word.

   ☐

8. Add **est** to **cold** to make a new word.

   ☐

9. Circle the word that needs a capital letter.

   Yesterday was friday.

10. Write the number which shows where the full stop goes. ☐

    You love your mum
      3   2   1   4

DAY 31

1. Write the next letter.

q r s t ☐

2. What small letter goes with **U**?

a u e o | U | |

3. Tomorrow will be

[_____].

4. How many syllables in **house**? ☐

5. Change **g** in **rag** to **t** to make a new word.

[_____]

6. Which two words sound the same?

bee go to be

7. Circle the word that rhymes with **seed**.

so need been nut

8. Circle the correct word.

The dog **ran/run** away.

9. What is missing from the question? Write it.

How are you today

. ?

10. Write the first word correctly.

soon I will be six years old.

[_____]

DAY 32

1. Write the next letter.

b c d e ☐

2. What small letter goes with **F**?

i f h t | F | |

3. Yesterday was

[_____].

4. How many syllables in **lady**? ☐

5. Change **b** in **rob** to **d** to make a new word.

[_____]

6. Which two words sound the same?

where two tip to

7. Circle the word that rhymes with **small**.

no one ball send

8. Circle the correct word.

Put the **bog/box** there.

9. What is missing from the question? Write it.

Is this your dog

. ?

10. Write the first word correctly.

look at the funny clown.

[_____]

UNIT 4

UNIT 4

DAY 33

1. Write the next letter.

f g h i ☐

2. What small letter goes with ***J***?

j i g n

J	

3. Today is ______________.

4. How many syllables in ***ladder***? ☐

5. Change ***t*** in ***root*** to ***m*** to make a new word.

6. Which word sounds the same as ***see***?

of sea has wig

7. Circle the word that rhymes with ***be***.

bin she you says

8. Circle the correct word.

We put the **dog/fog** outside.

9. What is missing from the question? Write it.

What is your name

. ?

10. Write the first word correctly.

her mum came to tea.

MY SCORE

DAY 34

1. Write the next letter.

i j k l ☐

2. What small letter goes with ***M***?

d v n m

M	

3. In two days it will be ______________.

4. How many syllables in ***October***? ☐

5. Change ***m*** in ***room*** to ***f*** to make a new word.

6. Which word sounds the same as ***by***?

he Dad are buy

7. Circle the word that rhymes with ***land***.

there balls and look

8. Circle the correct word.

He just got **buck/back**.

9. What is missing from the question? Write it.

How old are you

. ?

10. Write the first word correctly.

one day, a little boy found a book.

MY SCORE

DAY 35

1. Write the next letter.

   a　b　

2. What small letter goes with **C**?

   b　c　s　o　　| C | |

3. Yesterday was

   [   ] .

4. How many syllables in **animal**? [ ]

5. Change **d** in **bed** to **g** to make a new word.

   [   ]

6. Which word sounds the same as **blue**?

   our　had　blew　ask

7. Circle the word that rhymes with **box**.

   fox　big　school　were

8. Circle the correct word.

   Granny went to the **shop/shup**.

9. What is missing from the question? Write it.

   Where are you going

   　　　　　.　?

10. Write the first word correctly.

    you are my best friend.

    [   ]

MY SCORE

DAY 36

1. Write the next letter.

   d　e　f　

2. What small letter goes with **G**?

   g　j　p　t　　| G | |

3. Today is

   [   ] .

4. How many syllables in **pan**? [ ]

5. Change **s** in **has** to **d** to make a new word.

   [   ]

6. Which word sounds the same as **i**?

   egg　put　his　eye

7. Circle the word that rhymes with **tree**.

   took　see　net　there

8. Circle the correct word.

   The farmer had **maddy/muddy** boots.

9. What is missing from the question? Write it.

   Who are you

   　　　　　.　?

10. Write the first word correctly.

    they came to our house.

    [   ]

MY SCORE

DAY 37

1. Write the next letter.

   i j k ☐

2. What small letter goes with **L**?

   i e l w | L | |

3. Yesterday was

   _____ .

4. How many syllables in **pet**? ☐

5. Change **n** in **been** to **p** to make a new word.

   _____

6. Which word sounds the same as **sun**?

   today bus rug son

7. Circle the word that rhymes with **hug**.

   rug hoof big by

8. Circle the correct word.

   Joe has a **mossy/messy** bedroom.

9. What is missing from the question? Write it.

   Why are you doing that

   .   ?

10. Write the first word correctly.

    shut the door.

    _____

MY SCORE

DAY 38

1. Write the next letter.

   m n o ☐

2. What small letter goes with **P**?

   g c b p | P | |

3. Tomorrow will be

   _____ .

4. How many syllables in **pot**? ☐

5. Change **p** in **tip** to **n** to make a new word.

   _____

6. Which word sounds the same as **too**?

   got to she love

7. Circle the word that rhymes with **vet**.

   vase pet pull shut

8. Circle the correct word.

   The rocket was in the **pork/park**.

9. What is missing from the question? Write it.

   When can you play

   .   ?

10. Write the first word correctly.

    each boy gets a ball.

    _____

MY SCORE

DAY 39

1. Write the next letter.

u   v   w   ☐

2. What small letter goes with **X**?

z   k   x   y | **X** | |

3. Yesterday was

☐ .

4. How many syllables in **window**? ☐

5. Change **d** in **feed** to **t** to make a new word.

☐

6. Which word sounds the same as **four**?

fly   we   off   for

7. Circle the word that rhymes with **bin**.

soon   be   win   once

8. Circle the correct word.

I put **mill/milk** in my tea.

9. What is missing from the question? Write it.

Will you play with me

.   ?

10. Write the first word correctly.

your dad is funny.

☐

MY SCORE ◯

DAY 40

1. Write the next letter.

p   q   r   ☐

2. What small letter goes with **S**?

r   s   e   c | **S** | |

3. Yesterday was

☐ .

4. How many syllables in **because**? ☐

5. Change **k** in **book** to **t** to make a new word.

☐

6. Which word sounds the same as **meet**?

end   said   meat   ask

7. Circle the word that rhymes with **moon**.

Mum   push   was   soon

8. Circle the correct word.

The kite hit the **will/wall**.

9. What is missing from the question? Write it.

Who will you go with

.   ?

10. Write the first word correctly.

some cooks make hot food.

☐

MY SCORE ◯

DAY 41

1. What letter is missing?

   v   w   x   ☐   z

2. Write the capital letter that goes with **y**. ☐

3. Which word is correct?

   ○ September   ○ Sepptemmber

4. How many syllables in **bus**? ☐

5. Fill in **sh** or **ch**.

   ☐ell

6. Circle the correct spelling.

   Munday   Monday

7. Find a small word in **yellow**.

   ☐

8. The opposite of **fast** is:

   ○ clean   ○ slow

9. Fill in **When** or **What**.

   ☐ are you going to town?

10. Tick what is missing from the sentence.

    The zoo looks after lots of birds

    ○ capital letter   ○ full stop

DAY 42

1. What letter is missing?

   p   q   ☐   s   t

2. Write the capital letter that goes with **r**. ☐

3. Which word is correct?

   ○ October   ○ Oktober

4. How many syllables in **Mum**? ☐

5. Fill in **sh** or **ch**.

   ☐urch

6. Which word is correct?

   Tuesday   Tusday

7. Find a small word in **little**.

   ☐

8. The opposite of **first** is:

   ○ second   ○ last

9. Fill in **When** or **What**.

   ☐ is the name of that book?

10. Tick what is missing from the sentence.

    My bed is soft

    ○ capital letter   ○ full stop

DAY 43

1. What letter is missing?

    r   s   t   ☐   v

2. Write the capital letter that goes with **u**. ☐

3. Which word is correct?

    ☐ Noovemmber   ☐ November

4. How many syllables in **family**? ☐

5. Fill in **sh** or **ch**.

    ☐est

6. Circle the correct spelling.

    Wednesday   Wendsday

7. Find a small word in **came**.

    ☐

8. The opposite of **happy** is:

    ☐ sad   ☐ funny

9. Fill in **Why** or **Who**.

    ☐ did you do that?

10. Tick what is missing from the sentence.

    Here are some small mugs

    ☐ capital letter   ☐ full stop

DAY 44

1. What letter is missing?

    k   l   m   ☐   o

2. Write the capital letter that goes with **n**. ☐

3. Which word is correct?

    ☐ Deesembar   ☐ December

4. How many syllables in **sorry**? ☐

5. Fill in **sh** or **ch**.

    ☐ark

6. Circle the correct spelling.

    Thersday   Thursday

7. Find a small word in **with**.

    ☐

8. The opposite of **warm** is:

    ☐ hot   ☐ cold

9. Fill in **Who** or **Why**.

    ☐ are you laughing?

10. Tick what is missing from the sentence.

    Mum says I can go on my own

    ☐ capital letter   ☐ full stop

UNIT 5

DAY 45

1. What letter is missing?

   h   i   j   [ ]   l

2. Write the capital letter that goes with **k**. [ ]

3. Which word is correct?

   ○ July   ○ Jooleye

4. How many syllables in **boot**? [ ]

5. Fill in **sh** or **ch**.

   [ ]imney

6. Circle the correct spelling.

   Friday   Fryday

7. Find a small word in **brown**.

   [   ]

8. The opposite of **up** is:

   ○ down   ○ under

9. Fill in **Why** or **Who**.

   [   ] are you going to town?

10. Tick what is missing from the sentence.

    You can put the toys away now

    ○ capital letter   ○ full stop

MY SCORE ( )

DAY 46

1. What letter is missing?

   e   f   g   [ ]   i

2. Write the capital letter that goes with **h**. [ ]

3. Which word is correct?

   ○ Aperill   ○ April

4. How many syllables in **November**? [ ]

5. Fill in **sh** or **ch**.

   fi[ ]

6. Circle the correct spelling.

   Satuday   Saturday

7. Find a small word in **will**.

   [   ]

8. The opposite of **dark** is:

   ○ light   ○ night

9. Fill in **Why** or **Who**.

   [   ] is your best friend?

10. Tick what is missing from the sentence.

    One day, there was a big storm

    ○ capital letter   ○ full stop

MY SCORE ( )

DAY 47

1. What letter is missing?

    a   b   c ☐ e

2. Write the capital letter that goes with **d**. ☐

3. Which word is correct?

    ☐ May   ☐ Mayy

4. How many syllables in **foot**? ☐

5. Fill in **sh** or **ch**.

    di☐

6. Circle the correct spelling.

    Sunday   Sonday

7. Find a small word in **want**.

    ☐

8. The opposite of **slow** is:

    ☐ fast   ☐ thin

9. Fill in **Where** or **When**.

    ☐ does Ryan live?

10. Tick what is missing from the sentence.

    If we push and pull, it will go

    ☐ capital letter   ☐ full stop

MY SCORE ⃝

DAY 48

1. What letter is missing?

    a ☐ c   d   e

2. Write the capital letter that goes with **b**. ☐

3. Which word is correct?

    ☐ Marrsh   ☐ March

4. How many syllables in **very**? ☐

5. Fill in **sh** or **ch**.

    lun☐

6. Circle the correct spelling.

    Munnday   Monday

7. Find a small word in **toy**.

    ☐

8. The opposite of **last** is:

    ☐ second   ☐ first

9. Fill in **Where** or **When**.

    ☐ is it time for lunch?

10. Tick what is missing from the sentence.

    They will come to your school

    ☐ capital letter   ☐ full stop

MY SCORE ⃝

1. What letter is missing?

   t   u   ☐   w   x

2. Write the capital letter that goes with **v**. ☐

3. Which word is correct?

   ◯ Joon   ◯ June

4. How many syllables in **shop**? ☐

5. Fill in **sh** or **ch**.

   pu___

6. Circle the correct spelling.

   Tuesday   Toosday

7. Find a small word in **open**.

   ☐

8. The opposite of **day** is:

   ◯ night   ◯ morning

9. Fill in **Where** or **Why**.

   ☐ did you put the toys?

10. Tick what is missing from the sentence.

    My friend gave me a gift

    ◯ capital letter   ◯ full stop

1. What letter is missing?

   o   p   ☐   r   s

2. Write the capital letter that goes with **q**. ☐

3. Which word is correct?

   ◯ Janyouarry   ◯ January

4. How many syllables in **chip**? ☐

5. Fill in **sh** or **ch**.

   tor___

6. Circle the correct spelling.

   Wednesday   Weddsday

7. Find a small word in **then**.

   ☐

8. The opposite of **clean** is:

   ◯ smelly   ◯ dirty

9. Fill in **Who** or **Why**.

   ☐ did the chicken cross the road?

10. Tick what is missing from the sentence.

    He can ask his dad to help

    ◯ capital letter   ◯ full stop

UNIT 5

MY SCORE

MY SCORE

DAY 51

1. What letter comes next?

   s   t   u   v ☐

2. Write the small letter that goes with **W**. ☐

3. Fill in the missing letter.

   Sep___ember

4. How many syllables in **make**? ☐

5. Change **a** in **man** to **e** to make a new word.

   ☐

6. Circle the mistake.

   The be went buzzing by.

7. Which word has an **ow** sound like **cow**?

   call   food   now   dry

8. Circle the word that is not needed.

   I am in first second class.

9. Fill in **is** or **are**.

   This ☐ a nice cake.

10. Circle what is missing from the question.

    Why are you here

    ?   .

DAY 52

1. What letter comes next?

   p   q   r   s ☐

2. Write the small letter that goes with **T.** ☐

3. Fill in the missing letter.

   Septem___er

4. How many syllables in **woke**? ☐

5. Change **e** in **pet** to **i** to make a new word.

   ☐

6. Circle the mistake.

   It was two hot yesterday.

7. Which word has an **ow** sound like **cow**?

   how   me   seen   roof

8. Circle the word that is not needed.

   I am going to thank my friend the.

9. Fill in **is** or **are**.

   The hat ☐ on your head!

10. Circle what is missing from the question.

    Is this your book

    !   ?   .

DAY 53

1. What letter comes next?

   g   h   i   j   ☐

2. Write the small letter that goes with **A**. ☐

3. Fill in the missing letter.

   Se___tember

4. How many syllables in **drip**? ☐

5. Change **i** in **big** to **a** to make a new word.

   ☐

6. Circle the mistake.

   We swam in the sae.

7. Which word has an **ow** sound like **cow**?

   sand   he   yes   howl

8. Circle the word that is not needed.

   Pat went want to the shop.

9. Fill in **is** or **are**.

   The cats ☐ in the garden.

10. Tick what is missing from the question.

    Where are you

    ☐ question mark   ☐ full stop

DAY 54

1. What letter comes next?

   a   b   c   d   ☐

2. Write the small letter that goes with **E**. ☐

3. Fill in the missing letter.

   Septembe___

4. How many syllables in **December**? ☐

5. Change **o** in **cot** to **u** to make a new word.

   ☐

6. Circle the mistake.

   The gift is very pritty.

7. Which word has an **ow** sound like **cow**?

   cook   down   into   call

8. Circle the word that is not needed.

   The cat ran under the in chair.

9. Fill in **is** or **are**.

   The cups ☐ in the press.

10. Tick what is missing from the question.

    How is your mum

    ☐ question mark   ☐ full stop

UNIT 6

DAY 55

1. What letter comes next?

   e   f   g   h   ☐

2. Write the small letter that goes with **L**. ☐

3. Fill in the missing letter.

   Oc__ober

4. How many syllables in **skin**? ☐

5. Change **u** in **bug** to **a** to make a new word.

   ☐

6. Circle the mistake.

   I blu up the balloon.

7. Which word has an **ow** sound like **cow**?

   one   hoof   owl   was

8. Circle the word that is not needed.

   I made under a big cake.

9. Fill in **is** or **are**.

   The boy ☐ not here.

10. Tick what is missing from the question.

    How did you do that

    ☐ question mark   ☐ full stop

DAY 56

1. What letter comes next?

   k   l   m   n   ☐

2. Write the small letter that goes with **O**. ☐

3. Fill in the missing letter.

   Octo__er

4. How many syllables in **Christmas**? ☐

5. Change **ai** in **rain** to **u** to make a new word.

   ☐

6. Circle the mistake.

   I got dirt in my iye.

7. Which word has an **ow** sound like **cow**?

   town   cry   done   zoo

8. Circle the word that is not needed.

   The dog fog was black and white.

9. Fill in **is** or **are**.

   The boys ☐ not here.

10. Circle what is missing from the question.

    Do you like this book

    !   ?   .

MY SCORE

MY SCORE

DAY 57

1. What letter comes next?

   q   r   s   t   ☐

2. Write the small letter that goes with **U**. ☐

3. Fill in the missing letter.

   Oct__ber

4. How many syllables in **pizza**? ☐

5. Change **oi** in **coin** to **a** to make a new word.

   ☐

6. Circle the mistake.

   The sonn got very hot.

7. Which word has an **ow** sound like **cow**?

   some   do   where   clown

8. Circle the word that is not needed.

   like My friend went to a party.

9. Fill in **is** or **are**.

   My friend ☐ in second class.

10. Tick what is missing from the question.

   Can I come too

   ◯ question mark   ◯ full stop

MY SCORE

DAY 58

1. What letter comes next?

   o   p   q   r   ☐

2. Write the small letter that goes with **S**. ☐

3. Fill in the missing letter.

   Octobe__

4. How many syllables in **were**? ☐

5. Change **ee** in **seen** to **u** to make a new word.

   ☐

6. Circle the mistake.

   My friend is fore years old.

7. Which word has an **ow** sound like **cow**?

   is   ask   brown   once

8. Circle the word that is not needed.

   The car was in small and red.

9. Fill in **is** or **are**.

   My friends ☐ in second class.

10. Circle what is missing from the question.

   Who is that

   !   ?   .

MY SCORE

DAY 59

1. What letter comes next?

   v   w   x   y   ☐

2. Write the small letter that goes with **Z**. ☐

3. Fill in the missing letter.

   Septem__er

4. How many syllables in **song**? ☐

5. Change **ea** in **head** to **i** to make a new word.

   _____

6. Circle the mistake.

   We had to meet at skool.

7. Which word has an **ow** sound like **cow**?

   go   crown   was   of

8. Circle the word that is not needed.

   The sun and moon are in down the sky.

9. Fill in **is** or **are**.

   The leaves _____ on the ground.

10. Circle what is missing from the question.

    Will you be able to come

    !   ?   .

MY SCORE

DAY 60

1. What letter comes next?

   a   b   ☐

2. Write the small letter that goes with **C**. ☐

3. Fill in the missing letter.

   __ctober

4. How many syllables in **brother**? ☐

5. Change **ea** in **meat** to **e** to make a new word.

   _____

6. Circle the mistake.

   Mum went tu the shop.

7. Which word has an **ow** sound like **cow**?

   crowd   my   said   of

8. Circle the word that is not needed.

   Mum is going to the very dentist.

9. Fill in **is** or **are**.

   The paint _____ in the shed.

10. Circle what is missing from the question.

    When is your birthday

    !   ?   .

MY SCORE

1. Write the number of syllables in **after**.

2. Fill in the missing letter.

   Novembe___

3. Write in **th** or **ch**.

   ___irty

4. Which word does not belong in this family? Draw a line under it.

   name   take   safe   had

5. Circle **true** or **false**.

   Dogs can bark.

6. Add **ed** to **sand** to make a new word.

7. Fill in **was** or **were**.

   Kevin 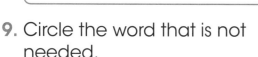 laughing.

8. Add **s** to **seed** to mean more than one.

9. Circle the word that is not needed.

   Dad likes pizza and looked chips.

10. Which word needs a capital letter?

    I love to sleep in on saturdays.

MY SCORE

1. Write the number of syllables in **loaf**.

2. Fill in the missing letter.

   No___ember

3. Write in **th** or **ch**.

   ___ird

4. Which word does not belong in this family? Draw a line under it.

   pipe   mice   under   bike

5. Circle **true** or **false**.

   A ball is like a square.

6. Add **ed** to **smash** to make a new word.

7. Fill in **was** or **were**.

   The children laughing.

8. Add **s** to **tree** to mean more than one.

9. Circle the word that is not needed.

   I think tennis is fun oven.

10. Which word needs a capital letter?

    The day I like best is sunday.

MY SCORE

UNIT 7

1. Write the number of syllables in **hospital.**

2. Fill in the missing letter.

   Novem___er

3. Write in *th* or *ch*.

   ___ank

4. Which word does not belong in this family? Draw a line under it.

   home   woke   hope   got

5. Circle **true** or **false**.

   My name is Rumpelstiltskin.

6. Add **ed** to **wish** to make a new word.

7. Fill in **was** or **were**.

   Rachel [   ] in her room.

8. Add **s** to **room** to mean more than one.

9. Circle the word that is not needed.

   Peter saw the pretty was flower.

10. Which word needs a capital letter?

    Our town is called newtown.

1. Write the number of syllables in **baby**.

2. Fill in the missing letter.

   N___vember

3. Write in *th* or *sh*.

   ___umb

4. Which word does not belong in this family? Draw a line under it.

   same   ate   had   spade

5. Circle **true** or **false**.

   My teacher has superpowers.

6. Add **ed** to **hint** to make a new word.

7. Fill in **was** or **were**.

   The parrots [   ] eating.

8. Add **s** to **mug** to mean more than one.

9. Circle the word that is not needed.

   Does every dog walk have a tail?

10. Which word needs a capital letter?

    I like living in ireland.

UNIT 7

MY SCORE

MY SCORE

1. Write the number of syllables in **where**.

2. Fill in the missing letter.

   ___ovember

3. Write in **sh** or **th**.

   pa___

4. Which word does not belong in this family? Draw a line under it.

   tie   lie   cried   pie   spin

5. Circle **true** or **false**.

   Two boxes have two lids.

6. Add **ed** to **plant** to make a new word.

7. Fill in **was** or **were**.

   The kitten _____ looking for milk.

8. Add **s** to **jug** to mean more than one.

9. Circle the word that is not needed.

   The baby wanted over his bottle.

10. Which word needs a capital letter?

    Our pet fish is called finn.

1. Write the number of syllables in **that**.

2. Fill in the missing letter.

   Decembe___

3. Write in **sh** or **th**.

   tee___

4. Draw a line under the word that makes a different **ie** sound.

   pie   thief   field   chief

5. Circle **true** or **false**.

   A week has twenty-five days.

6. Add **ed** to **camp** to make a new word.

7. Fill in **was** or **were**.

   Grandad _____ in the car.

8. Add **s** to **pot** to mean more than one.

9. Circle the word that is not needed.

   The girl ran cooked after the white kite.

10. Which word needs a capital letter?

    My sister, sarah, made me a sandwich.

UNIT 7

1. Write the number of syllables in **honey**.

2. Fill in the missing letter.
   Decem___er

3. Write in **sh** or **th**.
   ___ark

4. Which word does not belong in this family? Draw a line under it.
   high   night   grip   light

5. Circle **true** or **false**.
   Christmas is in December.

6. Add **ed** to **jump** to make a new word.

7. Fill in **was** or **were**.
   Mum and Dad ___ going to a party.

8. Add **s** to **tin** to mean more than one.

9. Circle the word that is not needed.
   I saw the film in open my friend's house.

10. Which word needs a capital letter?
    I made a cake for Mrs smith.

1. Write the number of syllables in **dry**.

2. Fill in the missing letter.
   Dece___ber

3. Write in **sh** or **th**.
   ___em

4. Which word does not belong in this family? Draw a line under it.
   bone   wore   sore   more

5. Circle **true** or **false**.
   Lions love to eat carrots.

6. Add **ed** to **bump** to make a new word.

7. Fill in **was** or **were**.
   Adam ___ first in the race.

8. Add **s** to **boot** to mean more than one.

9. Circle the word that is not needed.
   Where does a rainbow go funny?

10. Which word needs a capital letter?
    My friend lives in england.

MY SCORE

MY SCORE

1. Write the number of syllables in **seen**.

2. Fill in the missing letter.

   D__cember

3. Write in **sh** or **th**.

   di__

4. Which word does not belong in this family? Draw a line under it.

   shore   yawn   draw   crawl

5. Circle **true** or **false**.

   I am in first class.

6. Add **ed** to **brush** to make a new word.

7. Fill in **was** or **were**.

   The car _____ red and shiny.

8. Add **s** to **fan** to mean more than one.

9. Circle the word that is not needed.

   Grandad said a funny thing make yesterday.

10. Which word needs a capital letter?

   I called my baby chick chirpy.

MY SCORE

1. Write the number of syllables in **put**.

2. Fill in the missing letter.

   Decem__er

3. Write in **sh** or **th**.

   __ark

4. Which word does not belong in this family? Draw a line under it.

   ride   like   drip   five

5. Circle **true** or **false**.

   An apple can only be green.

6. Add **ed** to **start** to make a new word.

7. Fill in **was** or **were**.

   My dog _____ barking.

8. Add **s** to **cake** to mean more than one.

9. Circle the word that is not needed.

   The red apple fell down over from the tree.

10. Which word needs a capital letter?

   We went to france.

MY SCORE

UNIT 7

1. Write **Septumbar** correctly.

2. Which word starts with **st** like **stop**?

   step   cost   skip   ship

3. Circle the word that ends with **ay** like **day**.

   lady   play   happy   your

4. Circle the word that rhymes with **wish**.

   shut   fish   ship   smash

5. Add **un** to **kind** to make a word that means 'not kind'.

6. Circle **true** or **false**.

   The colour of snow is white.

7. Fill in **has** or **have**.

   Paul a new schoolbag.

8. Add **es** to **brush** to mean more than one.

9. Fill in **to** or **two**.

   I went the shop yesterday.

10. Fill in **When** or **Who**.

    are you?

1. Write **Oktoeberr** correctly.

2. Which word starts with **sk** like **skin**?

   stand   skip   spot   disk

3. Circle the word that ends with **st** like **best**.

   stone   must   skip   bunch

4. Circle the word that rhymes with **chin**.

   chop   shop   chip   shin

5. Add **un** to **safe** to make a word that means 'not safe'.

6. Circle **true** or **false**.

   The colour of coal is black.

7. Fill in **has** or **have**.

   It rained all day.

8. Add **es** to **smash** to mean more than one.

9. Fill in **to** or **two**.

   I made chocolate cakes.

   2

10. Fill in **Who** or **Where**.

    did you go?

DAY 73

1. Write **Novambar** correctly.

2. Which word starts with **sw** like **swim**?

   spell   sweep   cows   nest

3. Circle the word that ends with **mp** like **lump**.

   map   cost   swing   camp

4. Circle the word that rhymes with **drip**.

   grub   grip   drum   try

5. Add **un** to **well** to make a word that means 'not well' or 'sick'.

6. Circle **true** or **false**.

   A mouse is taller than a giraffe.

7. Fill in **has** or **have**.

   We [   ] a new car.

8. Add **es** to **punch** to mean more than one.

9. Fill in **to** or **two**.

   We have [   ] walk in pairs.

10. Fill in **When** or **Where**.

    [   ] do you think they are?

DAY 74

1. Write **Deesember** correctly.

2. Which word starts with **sl** like **sleep**?

   speak   slip   sweet   gulls

3. Circle the word that ends with **ng** like **song**.

   gun   hang   lost   give

4. Circle the word that rhymes with **chop**.

   shop   much   rich   sheep

5. Add **un** to **happy** to make a word that means 'not happy'.

6. Circle **true** or **false**.

   A book can be big or small.

7. Fill in **has** or **have**.

   The dog [   ] puppies.

8. Add **es** to **lunch** to mean more than one.

9. Fill in **to** or **two**.

   I have [   ] pencils in my pencil case.

10. Fill in **Who** or **Why**.

    [   ] are you doing that?

UNIT 8

DAY 75

1. Today is

    _____ .

2. Which word starts with **dr** like **drum**?

    does   made   those   drip

3. Circle the word that ends with **er** like **paper**.

    bird   never   rich   sheet

4. Circle the word that rhymes with **camp**.

    jump   lamp   tent   spade

5. Add **un** to **like** to make a word that means 'not alike'.

    _____

6. Circle **true** or **false**.

    Our school is under the ground.

7. Fill in **has** or **have**.

    My copy _____ lots of pages.

8. Add **es** to **church** to mean more than one.

    _____

9. Fill in **to** or **two**.
    Granny gave me

    _____ biscuits.

10. Fill in **What** or **Who**.

    _____ are you buying?

MY SCORE

DAY 76

1. Yesterday was

    _____ .

2. Which word starts with **gr** like **grub**?

    grip   once   brush   sing

3. Circle the word that ends with **ar** like **car**.

    girl   your   star   over

4. Circle the word that rhymes with **such**.

    much   chest   each   chick

5. Add **un** to **pack** to make the opposite of **pack**.

    _____

6. Circle **true** or **false**.

    Chocolate bars grow on trees.

7. Fill in **has** or **have**.

    Hens _____ two wings.

8. Add **es** to **beach** to mean more than one.

    _____

9. Fill in **to** or **two**.

    I have _____ ham sandwiches for lunch.

10. Fill in **Who** or **Which**.

    _____ one would you like?

MY SCORE

UNIT 8

DAY 77

1. Tomorrow will be

   _____.

2. Which word starts with *tr* like *trip*?

   crib   try   creep   sheet

3. Circle the word that ends with *oy* like *boy*.

   very   toy   crab   my

4. Circle the word that rhymes with *lost*.

   list   no   cost   love

5. Add *un* to *fair* to make a word that means 'not fair'.

   _____

6. Circle *true* or *false*.

   A clock shows the time.

7. Fill in *has* or *have*.

   They _____ a new computer.

8. Add *es* to *bush* to mean more than one.

   _____

9. Fill in *to* or *two*.

   Can we go _____ the pool?

10. Fill in *Who* or *Which*.

    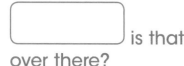

    _____ is that over there?

DAY 78

1. Last month was

   _____.

2. Which word starts with *br* like *bring*?

   thing   dress   below   brave

3. Circle the word that ends with *ow* like *blow*.

   were   block   our   snow

4. Circle the word that rhymes with *skin*.

   spent   spin   skip   one

5. Add *un* to *tidy* to make a word that means 'not tidy'.

   _____

6. Circle *true* or *false*.

   Orange juice is made from bananas.

7. Fill in *has* or *have*.

   The children _____ lots of sweets.

8. Add *es* to *witch* to mean more than one.

   _____

9. Fill in *to* or *two*.

   The _____ puppies are barking.

10. Fill in *What* or *How*.

    _____ is in the bag?

MY SCORE

MY SCORE

UNIT 8

DAY 79

1. Two days ago was

   _____.

2. Which word starts with **cr** like **crab**?

   crib   lunch   came   grab

3. Circle the word that ends with **ew** like **new**.

   now   flew   blue   summer

4. Circle the word that rhymes with **ant**.

   bump   went   plant   hint

5. Add **un** to **lucky** to make a word that means 'not lucky'.

   _____

6. Circle **true** or **false**.

   We get homework on Friday.

7. Fill in **has** or **have**.

   Kate _____ a nice jumper.

8. Add **es** to **buzz** to mean more than one.

   _____

9. Fill in **to** or **two**.
   Can you take me _____ school?

10. Fill in **Why** or **Where**.

   _____ are we going this way?

MY SCORE

DAY 80

1. Tomorrow will be

   _____.

2. Which word starts with **sp** like **spell**?

   bring   lost   bell   spot

3. Circle the word that ends with **ue** like **clue** and **true**.

   crow   blue   grew   winter

4. Circle the word that rhymes with **beach**.

   I   love   chip   teach

5. Add **un** to **fair** to make a word that means 'not fair'.

   _____

6. Circle **true** or **false**.

   Chocolate cake makes you clever.

7. Fill in **has** or **have**.

   Mum and Dad _____ to go to town.

8. Add **es** to **glass** to mean more than one.

   _____

9. Fill in **to** or **two**.

   Do we have _____ sing now?

10. Fill in **Where** or **How many**.

   _____ pencils do you have?

MY SCORE

UNIT 8

DAY 81

1. Fill in **bl** or **br**.

   ____ank

2. Which word **ends** with **ip** like **trip**, **skip**, **lip** and **ship**?

   grip   put   pie   party

3. Add **magic e** to **hat**.

4. Circle the word with **oo** in the middle like **food**, **pool** and **moon**.

   once   both   open   noon

5. Add **ball** to **foot** to make a compound word.

6. Add **ing** to **start** to make a new word.

7. Circle the correct word.

   The **witch/watch** saw the moon.

8. Put a dot where **and** is needed.

   Peter Paul are twins.

9. Write the first word correctly.

   turn the television off.

10. Write **?** or **!** at the end of the sentence.

    Be quiet

MY SCORE

DAY 82

1. Fill in **bl** or **br**.

   ____ack

2. Which word ends with **ell** like **fell**, **well**, **sell** and **spell**?

   wall   pull   shell   tail

3. Add **magic e** to **can**.

4. Circle the word with **oo** in the middle like **book**, **foot** and **wood**.

   clown   want   good   path

5. Add **ground** to **play** to make a compound word.

6. Add **ing** to **wish** to make a new word.

7. Circle the correct word.

   I sat at the **disk/desk**.

8. Put a dot where **and** is needed.

   He stopped looked.

9. Write the first word correctly.

   show the picture to your mum.

10. Write **?** or **!** at the end of the sentence.

    I won't do it

MY SCORE

DAY 83

1. Fill in **bl** or **br**.

   ___ick

2. Which word ends with **op** like **top**, **stop**, **hop** and **chop**?

   post   they   shop   today

3. Add **magic e** to **rip**.

4. Circle the word with **ir** in the middle like **girl**, **bird** and **shirt**.

   hurt   crib   sink   third

5. Add **yard** to **farm** to make a compound word.

6. Add **ing** to **stand** to make a new word.

7. Circle the correct word.

   The army had a **tank/thank.**

8. Put a dot where **and** is needed.

   Mum Dad were mad.

9. Write the first word correctly.

   does the baby ever sleep?

10. Write **?** or **!** at the end of the sentence.

    Give it to me now

MY SCORE

DAY 84

1. Fill in **bl** or **br**.

   ___ock

2. Which word ends with **in** like **skin**, **spin**, **chin** and **bin**?

   skip   nip   fin   said

3. Add **magic e** to **fin**.

4. Circle the word with **ur** in the middle like **turn**, **church** and **hurt**.

   burn   first   sink   runner

5. Add **room** to **bed** to make a compound word.

6. Add **ing** to **fish** to make a new word.

7. Circle the correct word.

   I put the **stomp/stamp** on the postcard.

8. Put a dot where **and** is needed.

   The ball is black white.

9. Write the first word correctly.

   put the ham on the bread.

10. Write **?** or **!** at the end of the sentence.

    Why did you do that

MY SCORE

UNIT 9

DAY 85

1. Fill in **bl** or **br**.

   ___other

2. Which word ends with **ap** like **clap**, **snap**, **flap** and **nap**?

   clip   chap   snip   paper

3. Add **magic e** to **hop**.

4. Circle the word with **er** in the middle like **very** and **herb**.

   term   first   burst   red

5. Add **berry** to **black** to make a compound word.

6. Add **ing** to **nest** to make a new word.

7. Circle the correct word.

   I found a **twin/twig** in the forest.

8. Put a dot where **and** is needed.

   The dog was big wet.

9. Write the first word correctly.

   why are you doing this?

10. Write **?** or **!** at the end of the sentence.

    Mum will be very mad

DAY 86

1. Fill in **bl** or **br**.

   ___ast

2. Which word ends with **im** like **swim**, **skim**, **trim** and **him**?

   jam   slim   mime   slip

3. Add **magic e** to **not**.

4. Circle the word with **ar** in the middle like **park** and **cart**.

   cook   mark   Thursday   rat

5. Add **bird** to **blue** to make a compound word.

6. Add **ing** to **teach** to make a new word.

7. Circle the correct word.

   Wipe your feet on the **mast/mats**.

8. Put a dot where **and** is needed.

   My friend I are playing.

9. Write the first word correctly.

   who is going to your party?

10. Write **?** or **!** at the end of the sentence.

    I don't believe you

UNIT 9

DAY 87

1. Fill in **bl** or **br**.

   ____ick

2. Which word ends with **ub** like **tub**, **rub**, **grub** and **stub**?

   but   scrub   cube   slab

3. Add **magic e** to **hug**.

4. Circle the word with **ow** in the middle like **down** and **fowl**.

   wood   won't   saw   town

5. Add **tub** to **bath** to make a compound word.

6. Add **ing** to **camp** to make a new word.

7. Circle the correct word.

   I like to eat a **stone / scone.**

8. Put a dot where **and** is needed.

   Clowns are funny silly.

9. Write the first word correctly.

   here is the brown dog.

10. Write **?** or **!** at the end of the sentence.

    Dad was so silly

MY SCORE

DAY 88

1. Fill in **bl** or **br**.

   Clue: sweep the floor.   ____ush

2. Which word ends with **op** like **top**, **hop**, **chop** and **shop**?

   flop   pot   chip   push

3. Add **magic e** to **tub**.

4. Circle the word with **oe** in the middle like **goes** and **toes**.

   love   joey   some   come

5. Add **day** to **birth** to make a compound word.

6. Add **ing** to **grow** to make a new word.

7. Circle the correct word.

   The red **ros / rose** smells lovely.

8. Put a dot where **and** is needed.

   This food is lumpy cold.

9. Write the first word correctly.

   once, there was a kind princess.

10. Write **?** or **!** at the end of the sentence.

    I won first prize

MY SCORE

DAY 89

1. Fill in **bl** or **br**.

   Clue: my face goes red _____ush

2. Which word ends with **ab** like **crab**, **grab**, **stab** and **flab**?

   bath   slab   rob   clap

3. Take away the **magic e** and write the new words.

   tape _____   cube _____

4. Circle the word with **ou** in the middle like **loud** and **foul.**

   go   school   shout   clown

5. Add **cake** to **pan** to make a compound word.

   [   ]

6. Add **ing** to **brush** to make a new word.

   [   ]

7. Circle the correct word.

   The rabbit is in the **hatch/hutch.**
   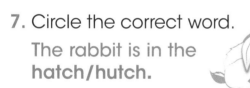

8. Put a dot where **and** is needed.

   My coat is soft warm.

9. Write the first word correctly.

   how did they do it?

   [   ]

10. Write **?** or **!** at the end of the sentence.

    Don't do that

DAY 90

1. Fill in **bl** or **br**.

   Clue: my eyes do this _____ink

2. Which word ends with **ing** like **king**, **sing**, **thing** and **bring**?

   hang   go   give   sting

3. Take away the **magic e** and write the new words.

   pipe _____   cute _____

4. Circle the word with **or** in the middle like **fork** and **torn**.

   sort   saw   rot   cloud

5. Add **hill** to **up** to make a compound word.

   [   ]

6. Add **ing** to **smash** to make a new word.

   [   ]

7. Circle the correct word.

   I saw the time on my **witch/ watch**.

8. Put a dot where **and** is needed.

   Ask see what she says.

9. Write the first word correctly.

   only one friend can go.

   [   ]

10. Write **?** or **!** at the end of the sentence.

    Silly me

MY SCORE

MY SCORE

UNIT 9

DAY 91

1. Fill in **cl** or **cr**.

   ___ip

2. How many syllables in the word **spell**? ☐

3. Write the first sound in **ship**, **shop**, **shut** and **shin**.

   ☐

4. Add **un** to **zip** to make a new word that means 'to open a zip'.

   ☐

5. Which word do **plays**, **playing**, **played** and **playground** start from?

   ☐

6. Add **s** to **pan** to write more than one.

   ☐

7. Add **es** to **bench** to write more than one.

   ☐

8. Circle the correct word.

   I have two **nets/nests** to catch fish.

9. Circle the word that needs a capital letter.

   The story has a crab called crusty.

10. Add **.**, **?** or **!** to the sentence.

    Why did I not get one

MY SCORE ◯

DAY 92

1. Fill in **cl** or **cr**.

   ___ab

2. How many syllables in the word **lamp**? ☐

3. Write the first sound in **chin**, **chop**, **chip**, **chick** and **chest**.

   ☐

4. Add **un** to **clean** to make a new word that means 'not clean'.

   ☐

5. Which word do **plants**, **planted** and **planting** start from?

   ☐

6. Add **s** to **vet** to write more than one.

   ☐

7. Add **es** to **torch** to write more than one.

   ☐

8. Circle the correct word.

   My hand can make a **fits/fist**.

9. Circle the word that needs a capital letter.

   The name of the film is aladdin.

10. Add **.**, **?** or **!** to the sentence.

    What day is it today

MY SCORE ◯

1. Fill in **cl** or **cr**.

___ub

2. How many syllables in **monkey**?

3. Write the first sound in **them**, **this**, **then**, **that**, **there** and **than**.

4. Add **un** to **load** to make a new word that means 'take away a load'.

5. Which word do **lands**, **landed** and **landing** start from?

6. Add **s** to **bin** to write more than one.

7. Add **es** to **switch** to write more than one.

8. Circle the correct word.

I love an ice-cream **cone/con**.

9. Circle the word that needs a capital letter.

My pet cat is called fluffy.

10. Add **.**, **?** or **!** to the sentence.

How long did it take to make that

MY SCORE

1. Fill in **cl** or **cr**.

___iff

2. How many syllables in **going**?

3. Write the first sound in **when**, **what**, **where**, **while** and **whip**.

4. Add **un** to **plug** to make a new word that means 'to take out the plug'.

5. Which word do **looks**, **looked** and **looking** start from?

6. Add **s** to **pot** to write more than one.

7. Add **es** to **match** to write more than one.

8. Circle the correct word.

Daddy started to **snor/snore**.

9. Circle the word that needs a capital letter.

Our pet fish is called spot.

10. Add **.**, **?** or **!** to the sentence.

What is the matter

MY SCORE

UNIT 10

DAY 95

1. Fill in **cl** or **cr**.

   ___ing

2. How many syllables in **help**? ☐

3. Write the letters making the first sound in **phone**, **photo** and **phantom**.

   [   ]

4. Add **un** to **fair** to make a new word that means 'not fair'.

   [   ]

5. Which word do **cooks**, **cooked**, **cooker** and **cooking** start from?

   [   ]

6. Add **s** to **bug** to write more than one.

   [   ]

7. Add **es** to **arch** to write more than one.

   [   ]

8. Circle the correct word.

   The flowers are in the **garten/ garden**.

9. Circle the word that needs a capital letter.

   Dear gran, I'm coming to visit you.

10. Add **.**, **?** or **!** to the sentence.

    Who took the cake

    MY SCORE

DAY 96

1. Fill in **cl** or **cr**.

   ___ush

2. How many syllables in **sing**? ☐

3. Circle the word that starts like **shop**.

   sheep   chick   than   whip

4. Add **un** to **lock** to make a new word that means 'to open'.

   [   ]

5. Which word do **bends**, **bending** and **bendy** start from?

   [   ]

6. Add **s** to **dot** to write more than one.

   [   ]

7. Add **es** to **fox** to write more than one.

   [   ]

8. Circle the correct word.

   The **vest/vets** helped the sick puppy.

9. Circle the word that needs a capital letter.

   Tell me what mum said.

10. Add **.**, **?** or **!** to the sentence.

    What is your name

    MY SCORE

UNIT 10

DAY 97

1. Fill in **cl** or **cr**.

   _____ust

2. How many syllables in **play**? ☐

3. Circle the word that starts like **cheek**.

   shirt   thank   white   chat

4. Add **un** to **able** to make a new word that means 'not able'.

   ☐

5. Which word do **teaching**, **teacher** and **teaches** start from?

   ☐

6. Add **s** to **hug** to write more than one.

   ☐

7. Add **es** to **bunch** to write more than one.

   ☐

8. Circle the correct word.

   I think the **best/bets** team will win.

9. Circle the word that needs a capital letter.

   Dad's first name is tom.

10. Write **.**, **?** or **!** at the end of the sentence.

    When are we going to the shop

MY SCORE

DAY 98

1. Fill in **cl** or **cr**.

   Clue: pain in my leg . _____amp

2. How many syllables in **turn**? ☐

3. Circle the word that starts like **think**.

   Thursday shock wheel chain

4. Add **un** to **hook** to make a new word that means 'to open or undo a hook'.

   ☐

5. Which word do **brushes** and **brushing** start from?

   ☐

6. Add **s** to **hand** to write more than one.

   ☐

7. Add **es** to **crash** to write more than one.

   ☐

8. Circle the correct word.

   The egg is going to **hutch/ hatch**.

9. Circle the word that needs a capital letter.

   I named my rabbit buster.

10. Write **.**, **?** or **!** at the end of the sentence.

    What time is it

MY SCORE

DAY 99

1. Fill in **cl** or **cr**.

   Clue: two cars hit each other ____ash

2. How many syllables in **father**? ☐

3. Circle the word that starts like **yes**, **yet**, **yellow**, **you** and **your**.

   Tuesday   yarn   then   they

4. Add **un** to **tie** to make a new word that means 'to undo what is tied up'.

5. Which word do **smashing**, **smashes** and **smashed** start from?

6. Add **s** to **ball** to write more than one.

7. Add **es** to **lash** to write more than one.

8. Circle the correct word.

   The castle was **scary/scory**.

9. Circle the word that needs a capital letter.

   We saw a clown called bobo.

10. Write **.**, **?** or **!** at the end of the sentence.

    How long is your hair

MY SCORE

DAY 100

1. Fill in **cl** or **cr**.

   Clue: funny person in the circus

   ____own

2. How many syllables in **brown**? ☐

3. Circle the word that starts like **photo**.

   phone   shout   whale   cheese

4. Add **un** to **lucky** to make a new word that means 'not lucky'.

5. Which word do **brings** and **bringing** start from?

6. Add **s** to **book** to write more than one.

7. Add **es** to **pinch** to write more than one.

8. Circle the correct word.

   These two children are **twigs/twins.**

9. Circle the word that needs a capital letter.

   She lives in italy.

10. Write **.**, **?** or **!** at the end of the sentence.

    How do you know his name

MY SCORE

Prim-Ed Publishing   www.prim-ed.com   New wave English in practice

UNIT 10

1. Fill in **fl** or **fr**.

   ___ip

2. How many syllables in the word **happy**? □

3. Change **th** in **thin** to **sh** to write a new word.

4. Circle the word that rhymes with **dear**.

   fear   desk   cart   thud

5. Add **ed** to **bang** to write a new word.

6. Add **ing** to **plant** to write a new word.

7. Which is correct?

   She **take/takes** a long bath.

8. Fill in **where** or **were**.

   I don't know ___ my book is.

9. Write **.**, **?** or **!** at the end of the sentence.

   This is SO boring

10. Circle the odd one out.

    mother   brother
    dad   grandad

1. Fill in **fl** or **fr**.

   ___og

2. How many syllables in the word **whip**? □

3. Change **ch** in **chick** to **th** to write a new word.

4. Circle the word that rhymes with **sang**.

   song   hang   school   go

5. Add **ed** to **play** to write a new word.

6. Add **ing** to **jump** to write a new word.

7. Which is correct?

   He **make/makes** me giggle.

8. Fill in **Where** or **Were**.

   ___ is my schoolbag?

9. Write **.**, **?** or **!** at the end of the sentence.

   Go away

10. Circle the odd one out.

    coat   scarf   gloves   T-shirt

DAY 103

1. Fill in **fl** or **fr**.

   ___om

2. How many syllables in the word **there**? ☐

3. Change **wh** in **when** to **th** to write a new word.

   ☐

4. Circle the word that rhymes with **rain**.

   car   says   train   one

5. Add **ed** to **train** to write a new word.

   ☐

6. Add **ing** to **bump** to write a new word.

   ☐

7. Which is correct?

   It **like/likes** me.

   ☐

8. Fill in **where** or **were**.

   The elephants ☐ in the zoo.

9. Write **.**, **?** or **!** at the end of the sentence.

   It's so exciting

10. Circle the odd one out.

    carrot   cabbage
    lorry   broccoli

MY SCORE ◯

DAY 104

1. Fill in **fl** or **fr**.

   ___at

2. How many syllables in the word **Monday**? ☐

3. Change **ch** in **chest** to **p** to write a new word.

   ☐

4. Circle the word that rhymes with **bump**.

   put   pull   are   lump

5. Add **ed** to **sail** to write a new word.

   ☐

6. Add **ing** to **hint** to write a new word.

   ☐

7. Which is correct?

   He **ride/rides** a horse.

   ☐

8. Fill in **where** or **were**.

   The cows ☐ in the field.

9. Write **.**, **?** or **!** at the end of the sentence.

   Help

10. Circle the odd one out.

    computer car train bus

MY SCORE ◯

UNIT 11

DAY 105

1. Fill in **fl** or **fr**.

____ask

2. How many syllables in the word **soon**? ☐

3. Change **st** in **stand** to **br** to write a new word.

[   ]

4. Circle the word that rhymes with **sing**.

some   ask   thing   being

5. Add **ed** to **wait** to write a new word.

[   ]

6. Add **ing** to **bring** to write a new word.

[   ]

7. Which is correct?

She **use/uses** a broom.

[   ]

8. Fill in **where** or **were**.

Do you know [   ] Sam lives?

9. Write **.**, **?** or **!** at the end of the sentence.

Stop doing that

10. Circle the odd one out.

sister   dad   granny   mum

MY SCORE

DAY 106

1. Fill in **fl** or **fr**.

____ost

2. How many syllables in the word **send**? ☐

3. Change **sk** in **skip** to **ch** to write a new word.

[   ]

4. Circle the word that rhymes with **bird**.

there   were   bath   third

5. Add **ed** to **turn** to write a new word.

[   ]

6. Add **ing** to **try** to write a new word.

[   ]

7. Which is correct?

The tap **drip/drips** a lot.

[   ]

8. Fill in **where** or **were**.

The teachers [   ] in the staffroom.

9. Write **.**, **?** or **!** at the end of the sentence.

I don't want any of it

10. Circle the odd one out.

brown   black   glass   pink

MY SCORE

DAY 107

1. Fill in **fl** or **fr**.

   ___ake

2. How many syllables in the word **look**? ☐

3. Change **m** in **made** to **sp** to write a new word.

   ☐

4. Circle the word that rhymes with **coat**.

   here   boat   sheet   crow

5. Add **ed** to **float** to write a new word.

   ☐

6. Add **ing** to **nest** to write a new word.

   ☐

7. Which is correct?

   He **trip/trips** over his shoelaces sometimes.

   ☐

8. Fill in **where** or **were**.

   I want to know

   ☐ the shop is.

9. Add **.**, **?** or **!** to the sentence.

   He is SO sorry

10. Circle the odd one out.

    helmet   doctor
    teacher   dentist

MY SCORE

DAY 108

1. Fill in **fl** or **fr**.

   Clue: part of fire   ___ame

2. How many syllables in the word **present**? ☐

3. Change **br** in **brim** to **sw** to write a new word.

   ☐

4. Circle the word that rhymes with **grow**.

   show   cow   grub   once

5. Add **ed** to **coat** to write a new word.

   ☐

6. Add **ing** to **swing** to write a new word.

   ☐

7. Which is correct?

   She **bring/brings** an apple every day.

   ☐

8. Fill in **where** or **were**.

   We ☐ in senior infants last year.

9. Add **.**, **?** or **!** to the sentence.

   Come back here, now

10. Circle the odd one out.

    lion rainbow tiger cheetah

MY SCORE

UNIT 11

DAY 109

1. Fill in **fl** or **fr**.

   Clue: not stale ____esh

2. How many syllables in the word **dish**? ☐

3. Change **sl** in **sleep** to **sh** to write a new word.

   ☐

4. Circle the word that rhymes with **brown**.

   clown   moon   by   both

5. Add **ed** to **rain** to write a new word.

   ☐

6. Add **ing** to **sweep** to write a new word.

   ☐

7. Which is correct?

   The wind blow/blows the tree.

   ☐

8. Fill in **where** or **were**.

   The presents ☐ under the bed.

9. Write **.**, **?** or **!** at the end of the sentence.

   Give that to me now

10. Circle the odd one out.

    tennis   football
    painting   rugby

MY SCORE ○

DAY 110

1. Fill in **fl** or **fr**.

   Clue: on your skin ____esh

2. How many syllables in the word **rich**? ☐

3. Change **dr** in **dress** to **ch** to write a new word.

   ☐

4. Circle the word that rhymes with **found**.

   where   around   float   don't

5. Add **ed** to **show** to write a new word.

   ☐

6. Add **ing** to **ask** to write a new word.

   ☐

7. Which is correct?

   She start/starts school today.

   ☐

8. Fill in **where** or **were**.

   I know ☐ the sweets are hidden.

9. Write **.**, **?** or **!** at the end of the sentence.

   It was SO sad

10. Circle the odd one out.

    nest kennel hutch dentist

MY SCORE ○

DAY 111

1. Fill in **dr** or **tr**.

   _____ink

2. How many syllables in the word **kite**? ☐

3. Which word ends with the same sound as **very**, **happy** and **silly**?

   party   do   you   are

4. Add **corn** to **pop** to make a new word.

   ☐

5. Circle the word with **air**.

   push   dear   stare   hair

6. Circle the word with **ear**.

   push   one   hear   care

7. Read the clue. Circle the word.

   A place where teachers and children go.

   school   station   museum

8. Read the clue then pick the **ending**.

   Clue: seen on a beach

   sh_____   ell   ill

9. Pick **and** or **but**.

   The cat ☐ dog are friends.

10. Write the first word correctly.

    when are we going to Gran's house?

    ☐

DAY 112

1. Fill in **dr** or **tr**.

   _____ank

2. How many syllables in the word **tube**? ☐

3. Which word ends with **ll** like **well**, **bell** and **fill**?

   whale   pull   silly   his

4. Add **saw** to **jig** to make a new word.

   ☐

5. Circle the word with **air**.

   wear   dare   pair   are

6. Circle the word with **ear**.

   near   air   were   says

7. Read the clue. Circle the word.

   A place where money is kept.

   library   bank   chemist

8. Read the clue then pick the **ending**.

   Clue: face goes red

   bl_____   osh   ush

9. Pick **and** or **but**.

   I played with my train

   ☐ car.

10. Write the first word correctly.

    what are you going to do?

    ☐

UNIT 12

DAY 113

1. Fill in **dr** or **tr**.

   ____uck

2. How many syllables in **trip**? ☐

3. Which word ends with **zz** like **buzz** and **fizz**?

   busy   zoom   fuzz   zebra

4. Add **man** to **snow** to make a new word.

   [ ]

5. Circle the word with **air** like **pair.**

   bird   fairy   said   no

6. Circle the word with **ear** like **near.**

   friend   year   meat   real

7. Read the clue. Circle the word.

   A place you go when you are sick.

   library   museum   hospital

8. Read the clue then pick the **ending**.

   Clue: to sweep the floor

   br_____   ash   ush

9. Pick **and** or **but**.

   [ ]

   She skipped _____ jumped along.

10. Write the first word correctly.

    where is your house?

    [ ]

MY SCORE ○

DAY 114

1. Fill in **dr** or **pr**.

   ____ill

2. How many syllables in **nest**? ☐

3. Which word ends with **ck** like **back** and **lick**?

   peck   cake   kitten   of

4. Add **bag** to **hand** to make a new word.

   [ ]

5. Circle the word with **air** like **fairy.**

   dear   four   aircraft   house

6. Circle the word with **ear** like **year**.

   your   where   fear   our

7. Read the clue. Circle the word.

   A place where you buy things.

   stable   shop   library

8. Read the clue then pick the **ending**.

   Clue: where our lungs are

   ch_____   est   ost

9. Pick **and** or **but**.

   [ ]

   He likes cats _____ dogs.

10. Write the first word correctly.

    while I sweep, you can dust.

    [ ]

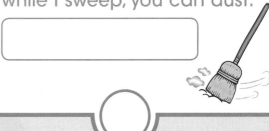

MY SCORE ○

DAY 115

1. Fill in *dr* or *tr*.

   ____ess

2. How many syllables in **spin**? ☐

3. Which word ends with **ss** like **kiss** and **miss**?

   says   off   sneak   mess

4. Add **house** to **light** to make a new word.

   [ ]

5. Circle the word with **air** like **pair**.

   dairy   family   here   mouse

6. Circle the word with **ear** like **fear**.

   tear   there   before   saw

7. Read the clue. Circle the word.

   A place where you go swimming.

   post office   stable   pool

8. Read the clue then pick the **ending**.

   Clue: after first and second

   th_____   erd   ird

9. Pick **and** or **but**.

   His shirt is black [ ] blue.

10. Write the first word correctly.

    this book has nice pictures.

    [ ]

DAY 116

1. Fill in *dr* or *tr*.

   ____affic

2. How many syllables in **jump**? ☐

3. Which word ends with a **v** sound like **give** and **live**?

   says   have   come   vat

4. Add **set** to **sun** to make a new word.

   [ ]

5. Circle the word with **air** like **dairy** that means a den for a wild animal.

   where   lair   ask   once

6. Circle the word with **ear** like **fear** that means tools or part of a machine.

   gear   house   was   some

7. Read the clue. Circle the word.

   A place where people pray.

   cinema   church   bank

8. Read the clue then pick the **ending**.

   Clue: worn on a king's head

   cr_____   own   uwn

9. Pick **and** or **but**.

   Dad yelled [ ] yelled.

10. Write the first word correctly.

    there once was a tiny elf.

    [ ]

DAY 117

1. Fill in **dr** or **tr**.

   Clue: Choo! Choo! ____ain

2. How many syllables in **river**? ☐

3. Which word ends with **nk** like **bank**, **think** and **honk**?

   kind   by   sunk   nick

4. Add **brush** to **hair** to make a new word.

   ☐

5. Circle the word with **air** like **lair** that means a chair on big wheels.

   she   wheelchair   put   her

6. Circle the word with **ear** like **gear** that means hair on the face.

   less   beard   cloud   we

7. Read the clue. Circle the word.

   A place that has art and paintings.

   hospital   museum   chemist

8. Read the clue then pick the **ending**.

   Clue: to see the time

   cl_____   ick   ock

9. Pick **and** or **but**.

   The dog was brown
   ☐ white.

10. Write the first word correctly.

    now I can see the pictures.

    ☐

DAY 118

1. Fill in **dr** or **tr**.

   Clue: Water goes down this. ____ain

2. How many syllables in **come**? ☐

3. Which word ends with **ff** like **puff**, **stiff** and **scoff**?

   find   cuff   the   for

4. Add **brush** to **tooth** to make a new word.

   ☐

5. Circle the word with **air** like **wheelchair**.

   are   burn   fear   hairy

6. Circle the word with **ear** like **beard** that means bright or easy to see.

   clear   her   they   go

7. Read the clue. Circle the word.

   A place that shows films.

   station   library   cinema

8. Read the clue then pick the **ending**.

   Clue: page with no writing

   bl_____   ink   ank

9. Pick **and** or **but**.

   He ☐ I are good friends.

10. Write the first word correctly.

    the end of the story was funny.

    ☐

UNIT 12

DAY 119

1. Fill in *dr* or *tr*.

   Clue: part of a tree _____unk

2. How many syllables in **thing**? ☐

3. Which word ends with *nt* like **tent, ant, hint** and **want**?

   ten   not   to   plant

4. Add **book** to **cook** to make a new word.

   ☐

5. Circle the word with *air* like **hairy**.

   has   stairs   my   school

6. Circle the word with *ear* like **clear** that means dull or gloomy.

   light   dreary   nice   me

7. Read the clue. Circle the word.

   A place where trains go.

   stable   station   school

8. Read the clue then pick the **ending**.

   Clue: place where people pray

   ch_____   erch   urch

9. Pick **and** or **but**.

   The boy ☐ girl were yawning.

10. Write the first word correctly.

    my teacher likes to sing.

    ☐

DAY 120

1. Fill in *dr* or *tr*.

   _____actor

2. How many syllables in **rain**? ☐

3. Which word ends with *th* like **tooth, path** and **both**?

   hat   think   today   bath

4. Add **time** to **bed** to make a new word.

   ☐

5. Circle the word with *air* like **stairs**.

   rain   high   hole   fair

6. Circle the word with *ear* like **dreary** that means the back or behind.

   before   so   rear   be

7. Read the clue. Circle the word.

   A place where you can borrow books.

   museum   hospital   library

8. Read the clue then pick the **ending**.

   Clue: sharp point on a bush

   th_____   orn   arn

9. Pick **and** or **but**. ☐

   It will rain today tomorrow.

10. Write the first word correctly.

    they are good football players.

    ☐

UNIT 12

DAY 121

1. Fill in *st* or *sp*.

   ___op

2. How many syllables in **over**? ☐

3. Change *th* in **path** to *ck* to make a new word.

   _____

4. Which word starts with *st* like **stand**?

   best   start   lost   cost

5. Add *er* to **quiet** to make a new word.

   _____

6. Add *est* to **quiet** to make a new word.

   _____

7. Add *s* to **cook** to mean more than one.

   _____

8. Add *es* to **catch** to mean more than one.

   _____

9. Circle the **naming word**.

   The man is tall.

10. Unjumble the sentence.

    dog likes My sausages

    _____

    _____

DAY 122

1. Fill in *st* or *sp*.

   ___ot

2. How many syllables in **grow**? ☐

3. Change *sh* in **smash** to *ck* to make a new word.

   _____

4. Which word starts with *sk* like **sky**?

   skull   disk   kids   love

5. Add *er* to **cheap** to make a new word.

   _____

6. Add *est* to **cheap** to make a new word.

   _____

7. Add *s* to **shop** to mean more than one.

   _____

8. Add *es* to **march** to mean more than one.

   _____

9. Circle the **naming word**.

   The rug is wet.

10. Unjumble the sentence.

    walks Mary to school

    _____

    _____

UNIT 13

1. Fill in **st** or **sp**.

   ___ade

2. How many syllables in **ask**? ☐

3. Change **ck** in **muck** to **sh** to make a new word.

   ☐

4. Which word starts with **sp** like **spin**?

   caps   spade   grasp   push

5. Add **er** to **weak** to make a new word.

   ☐

6. Add **est** to **weak** to make a new word.

   ☐

7. Add **s** to **ship** to mean more than one.

   ☐

8. Add **es** to **ditch** to mean more than one.

   ☐

9. Circle the **naming word**.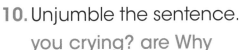

   I love my dog.

10. Unjumble the sentence.

    you crying? are Why

    _____

MY SCORE

1. Fill in **st** or **sp**.

   ___age

2. How many syllables in **down**? ☐

3. Change **p** in **chip** to **ck** to make a new word.

   ☐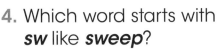

4. Which word starts with **sw** like **sweep**?

   wins   saw   sweet   was

5. Add **er** to **clean** to make a new word.

   ☐

6. Add **est** to **clean** to make a new word.

   ☐

7. Add **s** to **chip** to mean more than one.

   ☐

8. Add **es** to **box** to mean more than one.

   ☐

9. Circle the **naming word**.

   The knife is sharp.

10. Unjumble the sentence.

    is dinner? What for

    _____

MY SCORE

UNIT 13

DAY 125

1. Fill in *st* or *sp*.

   ___amp

2. How many syllables in **bunny**? ☐

3. Change *ng* in **song** to *ft* to make a new word.

   ☐

4. Which word starts with *sl* like **slap**?

   silly   said   less   slam

5. Add *er* to **clear** to make a new word.

   ☐

6. Add *est* to **clear** to make a new word.

   ☐

7. Add *s* to **chick** to mean more than one.

   ☐

8. Add *es* to **dress** to mean more than one.

   ☐

9. Circle the **naming word**.
   The car is small.

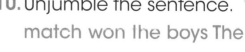

10. Unjumble the sentence.
    children The tennis love playing

   _____

DAY 126

1. Fill in *st* or *sp*.

   ___ick

2. How many syllables in **well**? ☐

3. Change *ll* in **spell** to *nd* to make a new word.

   ☐

4. Which word starts with *dr* like **drop**?

   red   hard   drag   do

5. Add *er* to **young** to make a new word.

   ☐

6. Add *est* to **young** to make a new word.

   ☐

7. Add *s* to **chest** to mean more than one.

   ☐

8. Add *es* to **class** to mean more than one.

   ☐

9. Circle the **naming word**.
   My dog likes barking.

10. Unjumble the sentence.
    match won the boys The

   _____

MY SCORE ○   MY SCORE ○

UNIT 13

DAY 127

1. Fill in **st** or **sp**.

   ____oon

2. How many syllables in **eleven**? ☐

3. Change **zz** in **buzz** to **s** to make a new word.

   [ ]

4. Which word starts with **gr** like **grab**?

   crab   car   girl   green

5. Add **er** to **high** to make a new word.

   [ ]

6. Add **est** to **high** to make a new word.

   [ ]

7. Add **s** to **home** to mean more than one.

   [ ]

8. Add **es** to **bush** to mean more than one.

   [ ]

9. Circle the **naming word**.

   The book fell down.

10. Unjumble the sentence.

    sausages Granny in put pan the

    _____

DAY 128

1. Fill in **st** or **sp**.

   ____ace

2. How many syllables in **beside**? ☐

3. Change **mp** in **jump** to **g** to make a new word.

   [ ]

4. Which word starts with **tr** like **trap**?

   there   tree   girl   two

5. Add **er** to **rich** to make a new word.

   [ ]

6. Add **est** to **rich** to make a new word.

   [ ]

7. Add **s** to **bone** to mean more than one.

   [ ]

8. Add **es** to **itch** to mean more than one.

   [ ]

9. Circle the **naming word**.

   The bus went by.

10. Unjumble the sentence.

    of Kim piece a cake ate

    _____

UNIT 13

MY SCORE

MY SCORE

DAY 129

1. Fill in **st** or **sp**.

   ___one

2. How many syllables in **roof**? ▢

3. Change **nt** in **hint** to **d** to make a new word.

   ▢

4. Which word starts with **br** like **brown**?

   but   by   brain   clown

5. Add **er** to **firm** to make a new word.

   ▢

6. Add **est** to **firm** to make a new word.

   ▢

7. Add **s** to **drum** to mean more than one.

   ▢

8. Add **es** to **grass** to mean more than one.

   ▢

9. Circle the **naming word**.

   The room is big.

10. Unjumble the sentence.

    cake teacher Our likes chocolate

    _____

    _____

MY SCORE

DAY 130

1. Fill in **st** or **sp**.

   ___able

2. How many syllables in **cook**? ▢

3. Change **ff** in **off** to **dd** to make a new word.

   ▢

4. Which word starts with **cr** like **cry**?

   crash   come   once   car

5. Add **er** to **clever** to make a new word.

   ▢

6. Add **est** to **clever** to make a new word.

   ▢

7. Add **s** to **nest** to mean more than one.

   ▢

8. Add **es** to **patch** to mean more than one.

   ▢

9. Circle the **naming word**.

   This is a big box.

10. Unjumble the sentence.

    horrible had My sandwiches friend

    _____

    _____

MY SCORE

DAY 131

1. Fill in **pl** or **pr**.

   ____ice

2. How many syllables in **dolphin**? ☐

3. Write the correct word: **wok** or **woke**.

   Pat _____ up early yesterday.

4. Which word starts with **gr** like **grain**?

   rag   crash   grass   they

5. Write the missing letter.

   M☐nday

6. Add **un** to **cut** to make a new word that means the opposite of **cut**.

   ☐

7. Circle the word with the same **ai** sound as **wait** and **train**.

   join   afraid   tie   said

8. Unjumble the sentence.

   does like rugby Jack not

   _____

   _____

9. Which is correct?

   He **wish/wishes** he had a pony.

   ☐

10. Circle the mistake.

    He did not know that i had one.

DAY 132

1. Fill in **pl** or **pr**.

   ____ace

2. How many syllables in **elephant**? ☐

3. Write the correct word: **rud** or **rude**.

   It is not nice to be _____ .

4. Which word starts with **tr** like **tramp**?

   track   rust   tired   to

5. Write the two missing letters.

   T☐☐sday

6. Add **un** to **fold** to make a new word that means the opposite of **fold**.

   ☐

7. Circle the word with **oi** like **oil** and **join.**

   rain   lion   point   the

8. Unjumble the sentence.

   across bridge ran the Molly

   _____

   _____

9. Which is correct?

   The ball **smash/smashes** the glass.

   ☐

10. Change the word that needs a capital letter.

    Today is monday.

UNIT 14

1. Fill in **pl** or **pr**.

   ____um

2. How many syllables in **alphabet**? ☐

3. Circle the word with **ir** in the middle like **first** and **firm**.

   rim   hurt   thirst   friend

4. Which word starts with **br** like **bring**?

   dress   rob   broom   pull

5. Write the missing letters.

   Wed ☐☐ sday

6. Add **un** to **dress** to make a new word that means the opposite of 'to dress'.

   ☐

7. Circle the word with **ee** like **tree** and **green**.

   she   sea   there   week

8. Unjumble the sentence.

   see in can the dark Cats

   _____

   _____

9. Which is correct?

   The boy **catch/catches** the ball.

   ☐

10. Circle the mistake.

    Tomorrow is tuesday.

1. Fill in **pl** or **pr**.

   ____ane

2. How many syllables in **you**? ☐

3. Circle the word with **ur** in the middle like **burst**, **curl** and **surf**.

   run   thirty   nurse   where

4. Which word starts with **cr** like **creep**?

   graph   rock   crawl   come

5. Write the two missing letters.

   Th ☐☐ sday

6. Add **un** to **clip** to make a new word that means the opposite of **clip**.

   ☐

7. Circle the word with **ea** like **meat** and **each**.

   see   dream   are   a

8. Unjumble the sentence.

   mice Four ran gate the under

   _____

   _____

9. Which is correct?

   Jill **fetch/fetches** a bucket of water.

   ☐

10. Circle the mistake.

    Yesterday was wednesday.

DAY 135

1. Fill in **pl** or **pr**.

   ____ant

2. How many syllables in **they**? ☐

3. Circle the word with **er** in the middle like **germ** and **herd**.

   perch   dirt   read   has

4. Which word starts with **fr** like **frog**?

   four   frost   rock   your

5. Write the missing letter.

   Fr ☐ day

6. Add **un** to **roll** to make a new word that means the opposite of **roll**.

   ☐

7. Circle the word with a **v** sound at the end like **live** and **love**.

   very   vest   gave   today

8. Unjumble the sentence.

   helps us read to teacher Our

   _____

   _____

9. Which is correct?

   The gardener **push/pushes** the wheelbarrow.

   ☐

10. Circle the mistake.

    I have football training on thursday.

    MY SCORE

DAY 136

1. Fill in **pl** or **pr**.

   ____int

2. How many syllables in **dinner**? ☐

3. Circle the word with **ar** in the middle like **mark** and **start**.

   smart   first   turn   ask

4. Which word starts with **cl** like **clip**?

   call   clock   lock   my

5. Write the two missing letters.

   Sat ☐☐ day

6. Add **un** to **seen** to make a new word that means 'not seen'.

   ☐

7. If **jump** + **er** = **jumper**, what does **hunt** + **er** make?

   ☐

8. Unjumble the sentence.

   My sits me friend beside best

   _____

   _____

9. Which is correct?

   The rash **itch/itches**.

   ☐

10. Circle the mistake.

    The last school day is friday.

    MY SCORE

UNIT 14

1. Fill in **pl** or **pr**.

   ____etty

2. How many syllables in **fish**?

3. Circle the word with **ow** in the middle like **clown** and **frown**.

   were   work   go   brown

4. Which word starts with **fl** like **flop**?

   loft   fall   flutter   pull

5. Write the missing letters.

   S ____day

6. Add **un** to **wind** to make a new word that means 'to undo'.

7. Circle the word with **ie** like **chief** and **thief**.

   was   I   field   ride

8. Unjumble the sentence.

   helped I clean kitchen the Dad

   _____

   _____

9. Which is correct?

   She often **brush/brushes** her hair.

10. Circle the mistake.

    We like to be lazy on sundays.

1. Fill in **pl** or **pr**.

   ____um

2. How many syllables in **pepper**?

3. Circle the word with **oe** like **woes** and **goes**.

   one   note   once   tiptoe

4. Which word starts with **ph** like **photo**?

   full   put   so   phone

5. Write the two missing letters.

   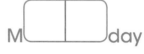
   M ____day

6. Add **un** to **block** to make a new word that means the opposite of **block**.

7. Circle the word with **igh** like **high** and **night**.

   hug   fly   his   bright

8. Unjumble the sentence.

   chips Dara and eating sausages loves

   _____

   _____

9. Which is correct?

   He **watch/watches** the waves roll in.

10. Circle the mistake.

    We went to spain on holidays.

DAY 139

1. Fill in **pl** or **pr**.

   ___ess

2. How many syllables in **five**? ☐

3. Circle the word with **ou** in the middle like **house** and **loud**.

   owl   cloud   down   you

4. Which word starts with **wh** like **where**, **what** and **when**?

   me   why   were   how

5. Write the three missing letters.

   Wed ☐☐☐ day

6. Add **un** to **made** to make a new word that means 'not made'.

   ☐

7. Circle the word with **or** like **short** and **horse**.

   rotten   morning   no   love

8. Unjumble the sentence.

   We going class are into second

   _____

   _____

9. Which is correct?

   My cat **arch/arches** her back.

   ☐

10. Circle the mistake.

    Mum and dad went on a picnic.

   MY SCORE

DAY 140

1. Fill in **pl** or **pr**.

   ___esent

2. How many syllables in **tune**? ☐

3. Circle the word with **or** in the middle like **horn** and **form**.

   hear   robot   short   today

4. Which word starts with **th** like **thin** and **third**?

   thick   teach   hold   put

5. Write the three missing letters.

   T ☐☐☐ day

6. Add **un** to **even** to make a new word that means 'not level'.

   ☐

7. Circle the word with **au** like **autumn** and **fault**.

   sauce   of   port   do

8. Unjumble the sentence.

   We teacher a will our miss lot

   _____

   _____

9. Which is correct?

   That scarf **match/matches** my bag.

   ☐

10. Circle the mistake.

    On saturday, we cleaned the house.

   MY SCORE

UNIT 12

DAY 141

1. Fill in **sm** or **sn**.

   ___ile

2. How many syllables in **pocket**? ☐

3. Change **oo** in **boot** to **oa** to write a new word.

   ☐

4. Add **er** to **faint** to make a new word.

   ☐

5. Add **est** to **faint** to make a new word.

   ☐

6. Circle the word with **are** like **care**.

   dare   read   ask   one

7. Draw a line under the **naming word**.

   The desk is messy.

8. Circle the correct spelling.

   woold   would

9. Another word for **mend** is:

   watch   fix   paint   cook

10. Write **.**, **?** or **!** at the end of the sentence.

   My dog is getting old

MY SCORE

DAY 142

1. Fill in **sm** or **sn**.

   ___ip

2. How many syllables in **rabbit**? ☐

3. Change **oo** in **book** to **ea** to write a new word.

   ☐

4. Add **er** to **fair** to make a new word.

   ☐

5. Add **est** to **fair** to make a new word.

   ☐

6. Circle the word with **are** like **dare**.

   read   friend   fare   of

7. Draw a line under the **naming word**.

   My doctor is nice.

8. Circle the correct spelling.

   before   befour

9. Another word for **lovely** is:

   scary   ugly   bossy   pretty

10. Write **.**, **?** or **!** at the end of the sentence.

   My baby sister has two teeth

MY SCORE

UNIT 15

New wave English in practice   72   www.prim-ed.com   Prim-Ed Publishing

1. Fill in **sm** or **sn**.

   ___ap

2. How many syllables in **carrot**? ☐

3. Change **oo** in **wood** to **ee** to write a new word.

   [   ]

4. Add **er** to **long** to make a new word.

   [   ]

5. Add **est** to **long** to make a new word.

   [   ]

6. Circle the word with **are** like **fare**.

   wear   car   were   bare

7. Draw a line under the **naming word**.

   Who owns this pencil?

8. Circle the correct spelling.

   tink   think

9. Another word for **roared** is:

   cried   laughed

   shouted   jumped

10. Write **.**, **?** or **!** at the end of the sentence.

    It is a fine, sunny day today

1. Fill in **sm** or **sn**.

   ___all

2. How many syllables in **thunder**? ☐

3. Change **oo** in **pool** to **ee** to write a new word.

   [   ]

4. Add **er** to **strong** to make a new word.

   [   ]

5. Add **est** to **strong** to make a new word.

   [   ]

6. Circle the word with **are** like **bare**.

   here   our   hare   the

7. Draw a line under the **naming word**.

   I like my teacher.

8. Circle the correct spelling.

   could   coud

9. Another word for **creepy** is:

   funny   scary

   bossy   pretty

10. Write **.**, **?** or **!** at the end of the sentence.

    The big, brown bear growled

MY SCORE

MY SCORE

DAY 145

1. Fill in **sm** or **sn**.

   ____ell

2. How many syllables in **sunset**? ☐

3. Change **ir** in **girl** to **oa** to write a new word.

   ☐

4. Add **er** to **young** to make a new word.

   ☐

5. Add **est** to **young** to make a new word.

   ☐

6. Circle the word with **are** like **hare**.

   how   mare   house   a

7. Draw a line under the **naming word**.

   The tiger ran away.

8. Circle the correct spelling.

   fownd   found

9. Another word for **yelled** is:

   shouted   cried

   said   talked

10. Write **.**, **?** or **!** at the end of the sentence.

   When is it lunchtime

DAY 146

1. Fill in **sm** or **sn**.

   ____ash

2. How many syllables in **kitchen**? ☐

3. Change **ur** in **hurt** to **oo** to write a new word.

   ☐

4. Add **er** to **plain** to make a new word.

   ☐

5. Add **est** to **plain** to make a new word.

   ☐

6. Circle the word with **are** like **mare**.

   more   rare   mouse   roost

7. Draw a line under the **naming word**.

   I live in a small house.

8. Circle the correct spelling.

   always   alwayz

9. Another word for **noticed** is:

   laughed   went

   saw   listened

10. Write **.**, **?** or **!** at the end of the sentence.

   Your tree has some fruit on it

MY SCORE

MY SCORE

UNIT 15

DAY 147

1. Fill in **sm** or **sn**.

   ___ore

2. How many syllables in **fetch**? ☐

3. Change **ow** in **brown** to **ai** to write a new word.

   [   ]

4. Add **er** to **great** to make a new word.

   [   ]

5. Add **est** to **great** to make a new word.

   [   ]

6. Circle the word with **are** like **rare**.

   said   do   share   before

7. Draw a line under the **naming word**.

   Do you know Tony?

8. Circle the correct spelling.

   wich   which

9. Another word for **gift** is:

   box   card

   present   letter

10. Write **.**, **?** or **!** at the end of the sentence.

    There is a lot of cloud today

DAY 148

1. Fill in **sm** or **sn**.

   ___oke

2. How many syllables in **notch**? ☐

3. Change **or** in **corn** to **oi** to write a new word.

   [   ]

4. Add **er** to **proud** to make a new word.

   [   ]

5. Add **est** to **proud** to make a new word.

   [   ]

6. Circle the word with **are** like **share**.

   she   scare   push   so

7. Draw a line under the **naming word**.

   I swam in the river.

8. Circle the correct spelling.

   once   wonce

9. Another word for **hungry** is:

   starving   sleepy

   thirsty   freezing

10. Write **.**, **?** or **!** at the end of the sentence.

    I can't stop laughing

UNIT 15

DAY 149

1. Fill in **sm** or **sn**.

    ___ow

2. How many syllables in **hutch**? ☐

3. Change **oi** in **soil** to **ea** to write a new word.

    ☐

4. Add **er** to **short** to make a new word.

    ☐

5. Add **est** to **short** to make a new word.

    ☐

6. Circle the word with **are** like **scare**.

    says   wore   sock   stare

7. Draw a line under the **naming word**.

    The film was funny.

8. Circle the correct spelling.

    reede   read

9. Another word for **replied** is:

    said   laughed

    walked   cried

10. Write **.** , **?** or **!** at the end of the sentence.

    The rabbit will sleep in the hutch

DAY 150

1. Fill in **sm** or **sn**.

    ___ail

2. How many syllables in **afraid**? ☐

3. Change **ou** in **shout** to **or** to write a new word.

    ☐

4. Add **er** to **loud** to make a new word.

    ☐

5. Add **est** to **loud** to make a new word.

    ☐

6. Circle the word with **are** like **stare**.

    pull   once   aware   was

7. Draw a line under the **naming word**.

    Can you open the door?

8. Circle the correct spelling.

    sede   siad   said

9. Another word for **angry** is:

    sad   rude

    mad   happy

10. Write **.** , **?** or **!** at the end of the sentence.

    What is that river called

MY SCORE

MY SCORE

1. What letter comes next?

   c   d   e   f   ☐

2. What capital letter goes with *p*?

   D   B   P   C   ☐

3. What comes next?
   Thursday …

   ◯ Saturday   ◯ Friday

4. Which word is correct?

   ◯ silly   ◯ sillee

5. Circle the word that begins with *j*.

   bug   go   jug   bin

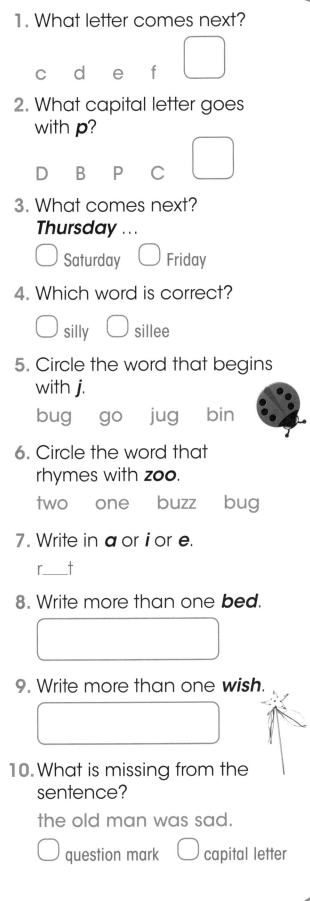

6. Circle the word that rhymes with **zoo**.

   two   one   buzz   bug

7. Write in *a* or *i* or *e*.

   r__t

8. Write more than one **bed**.

   ☐

9. Write more than one **wish**.

   ☐

10. What is missing from the sentence?

    the old man was sad.

    ◯ question mark   ◯ capital letter

11. What letter comes next?

    l   m   n   o   ☐

12. What capital letter goes with *m*?

    N   H   E   M   ☐

13. What comes next?
    Tuesday …

    ◯ Wednesday   ◯ Monday

14. Which word is correct?

    ◯ onderr   ◯ under

15. Circle the word that begins with *d*.

    bed   of   do   time

16. Circle the word that rhymes with **no**.

    off   done   so   up

17. Write in *a* or *i* or *e*.

    d__p

18. Write more than one **fin**.

    ☐

19. Write more than one **dish**.

    ☐

20. What is missing from the sentence?

    dad met Mum on the bus.

    ◯ question mark   ◯ capital letter

MY SCORE

REVISION

1. What letter comes first?

☐ g h i j

2. What small letter goes with **N**?

m n k z ☐

3. Which word is correct?

○ frend ○ friend

4. How many syllables in **puppy**? ☐

5. Change **m** in **meet** to **f** to make a new word.

[   ]

6. Write **Sonday** correctly.

[   ]

7. Add **ed** to **book** to make a new word.

[   ]

8. Add **ing** to **cook** to make a new word.

[   ]

9. Write in **a** or **e** or **u**.

n__p

10. What is missing from the sentence?

The girl is at school

○ full stop ○ question mark

11. What letter comes first?

☐ o p q r

12. What small letter goes with **C**?

s e o c ☐

13. Which word is correct?

○ again ○ agen

14. How many syllables in **September**? ☐

15. Change **b** in **bee** to **s** to make a new word.

[   ]

16. Write **Thersday** correctly.

[   ]

17. Add **ed** to **land** to make a new word.

[   ]

18. Add **ing** to **see** to make a new word.

[   ]

19. Write in **e** or **o** or **u**.

t__b

20. What is missing from the sentence?

They will come to our house

○ full stop ○ question mark

MY SCORE

1. What letter is missing?

   a   b   ☐   d   e

2. Which capital letter goes with *y*?

   K   W   C   Y   ☐

3. Today is

   ☐.

4. How many syllables in *music*? ☐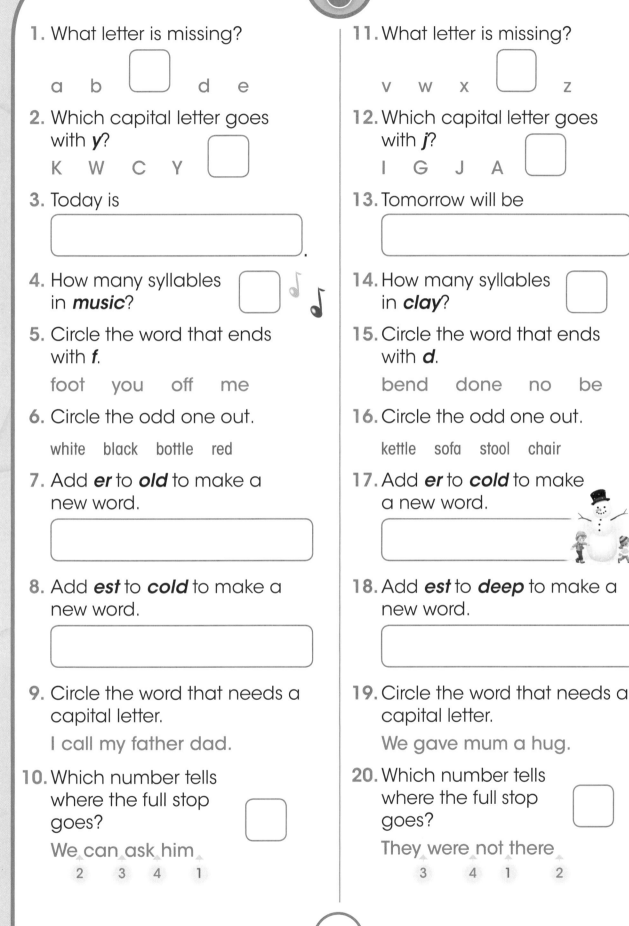

5. Circle the word that ends with *f*.

   foot   you   off   me

6. Circle the odd one out.

   white   black   bottle   red

7. Add *er* to *old* to make a new word.

   ☐

8. Add *est* to *cold* to make a new word.

   ☐

9. Circle the word that needs a capital letter.

   I call my father dad.

10. Which number tells where the full stop goes? ☐

    We can ask him
      2   3   4   1

11. What letter is missing?

    v   w   x   ☐   z

12. Which capital letter goes with *j*?

    I   G   J   A   ☐

13. Tomorrow will be

    ☐.

14. How many syllables in *clay*? ☐

15. Circle the word that ends with *d*.

    bend   done   no   be

16. Circle the odd one out.

    kettle   sofa   stool   chair

17. Add *er* to *cold* to make a new word.

    ☐

18. Add *est* to *deep* to make a new word.

    ☐

19. Circle the word that needs a capital letter.

    We gave mum a hug.

20. Which number tells where the full stop goes? ☐

    They were not there
      3   4   1   2

MY SCORE

REVISION

1. Write the next letter.

   a   b   [ ]

2. What small letter goes with **G**?

   g   j   p   t   [ ]

3. Today is

   [   ] .

4. How many syllables in **pot**? [ ]

5. Change **g** in **ping** to **k** to make a new word.

   [   ]

6. Which word sounds the same as **meet**?

   end   said   meat   ask

7. Circle the word that rhymes with **seed**.

   so   need   been   nut

8. Circle the correct word.

   Dad made/mode a cake.

9. What is missing from the question? Write it.

   What is your name

   .   ?

10. Write the first word correctly.

    one day, a little boy saw a book.

    [   ]

11. Write the next letter.

    d   e   f   [ ]

12. What small letter goes with **L**?

    i   e   l   w   [ ]

13. Tomorrow will be

    [   ] .

14. How many syllables in **animal**? [ ]

15. Change **k** in **book** to **m** to make a new word.

    [   ]

16. Which word sounds the same as **be**?

    a   bee   go   to

17. Circle the word that rhymes with **small**.

    no   one   ball   send

18. Circle the correct word.

    I want sume/some more cake.

19. What is missing from the question? Write it.

    How old are you

    .   ?

20. Write the first word correctly.

    you are my best friend.

    [   ]

MY SCORE

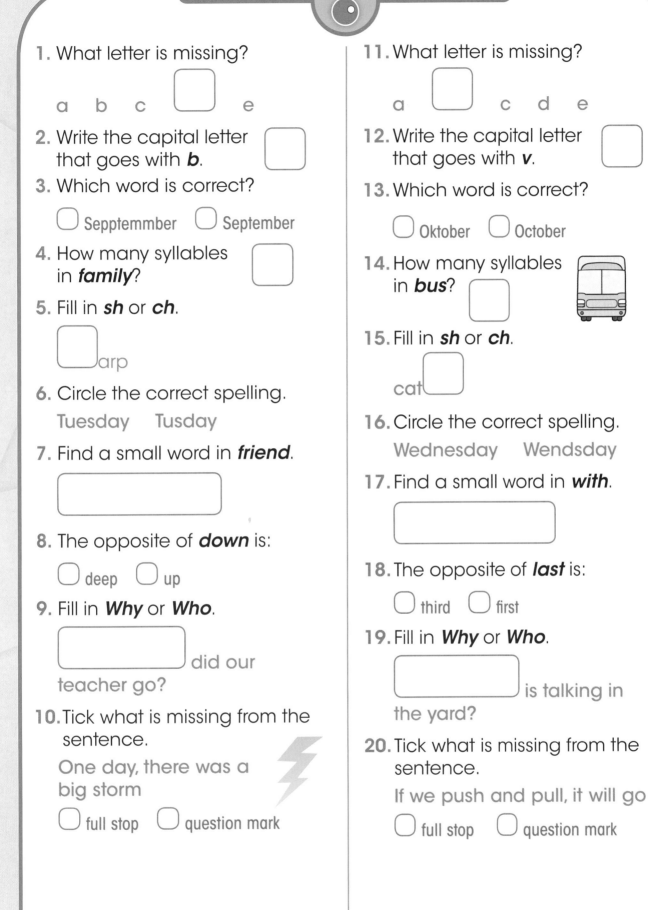

1. What letter is missing?

   a   b   c   ☐   e

2. Write the capital letter that goes with **b**. ☐

3. Which word is correct?

   ☐ Sepptemmber   ☐ September

4. How many syllables in **family**? ☐

5. Fill in **sh** or **ch**.

   ☐arp

6. Circle the correct spelling.

   Tuesday   Tusday

7. Find a small word in **friend**.

   ☐

8. The opposite of **down** is:

   ☐ deep   ☐ up

9. Fill in **Why** or **Who**.

   ☐ did our teacher go?

10. Tick what is missing from the sentence.

    One day, there was a big storm

    ☐ full stop   ☐ question mark

11. What letter is missing?

    a   ☐   c   d   e

12. Write the capital letter that goes with **v**. ☐

13. Which word is correct?

    ☐ Oktober   ☐ October

14. How many syllables in **bus**? ☐

15. Fill in **sh** or **ch**.

    cat☐

16. Circle the correct spelling.

    Wednesday   Wendsday

17. Find a small word in **with**.

    ☐

18. The opposite of **last** is:

    ☐ third   ☐ first

19. Fill in **Why** or **Who**.

    ☐ is talking in the yard?

20. Tick what is missing from the sentence.

    If we push and pull, it will go

    ☐ full stop   ☐ question mark

MY SCORE

1. What letter comes next?

   v   w   x   y   [ ]

2. Write the small letter that goes with **C**. [ ]

3. Fill in the missing letter.

   Septem__er

4. How many syllables in *pizza*? [ ]

5. Change *i* in **big** to **a** to make a new word.

   [   ]

6. Circle the mistake.

   The gift is very pritty.

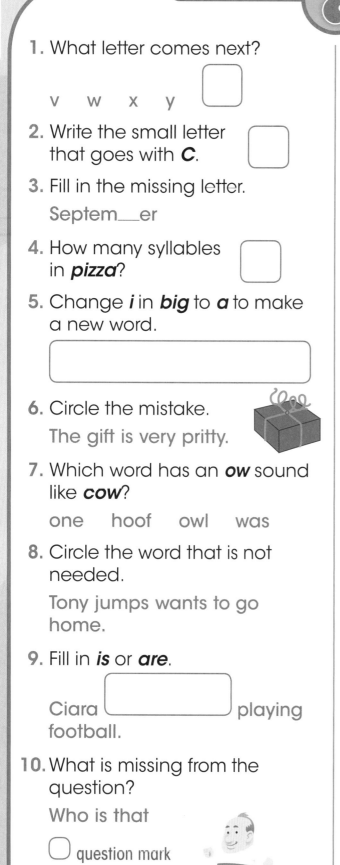

7. Which word has an *ow* sound like **cow**?

   one   hoof   owl   was

8. Circle the word that is not needed.

   Tony jumps wants to go home.

9. Fill in **is** or **are**.

   Ciara [   ] playing football.

10. What is missing from the question?

    Who is that

    ◯ question mark

    ◯ full stop

11. What letter comes next?

    a   b   [ ]

12. Write the small letter that goes with **W.** [ ]

13. Fill in the missing letter.

    Octo__er

14. How many syllables in **December**? [ ]

15. Change **o** in **cot** to **u** to make a new word.

    [   ]

16. Circle the mistake.

    I blue up the balloon.

17. Which word has an *ow* sound like **cow**?

    town   cry   done   zoo

18. Circle the word that is not needed.

    They had to push and puppy pull.

19. Fill in **is** or **are**.

    Emma and Sam

    [   ] in the garden.

20. Circle what is missing from the question.

    Will you be able to come

    !   ?   .

MY SCORE

1. Write the number of syllables in **after**. ☐

2. Fill in the missing letter.
   Novem___er

3. Write in **th** or **ch**.
   ___irty

4. Which word does not belong in this family? Draw a line under it.
   same   ate   had   spade

5. Circle **true** or **false**.
   A year has ten months.

6. Add **ed** to **camp** to make a new word.
   ☐

7. Fill in **was** or **were**.
   The classroom ☐ very cold.

8. Add **s** to write more than one **boot**.
   ☐
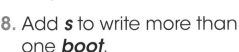

9. Circle the word that is not needed.
   The farmer had cows and hens on his orange farm.

10. Which word needs a capital letter?
    I want to go to france.
    ☐

11. Write the number of syllables in **hospital**. ☐

12. Fill in the missing letter.
    Dece___ber

13. Write in **sh** or **th**.
    tee___

14. Which word does not belong in this family? Draw a line under it.
    tie   lie   cried   pie   spin

15. Circle **true** or **false**.
    Camels live at the North Pole.

16. Add **ed** to **jump** to make a new word.
    ☐

17. Fill in **was** or **were**.
    The shops ☐ full of people.

18. Add **s** to write more than one **fan**.
    ☐

19. Circle the word that is not needed.
    We have maths keys for homework.

20. Which word needs a capital letter?
    I love to dance on mondays.
    ☐

MY SCORE

REVISION

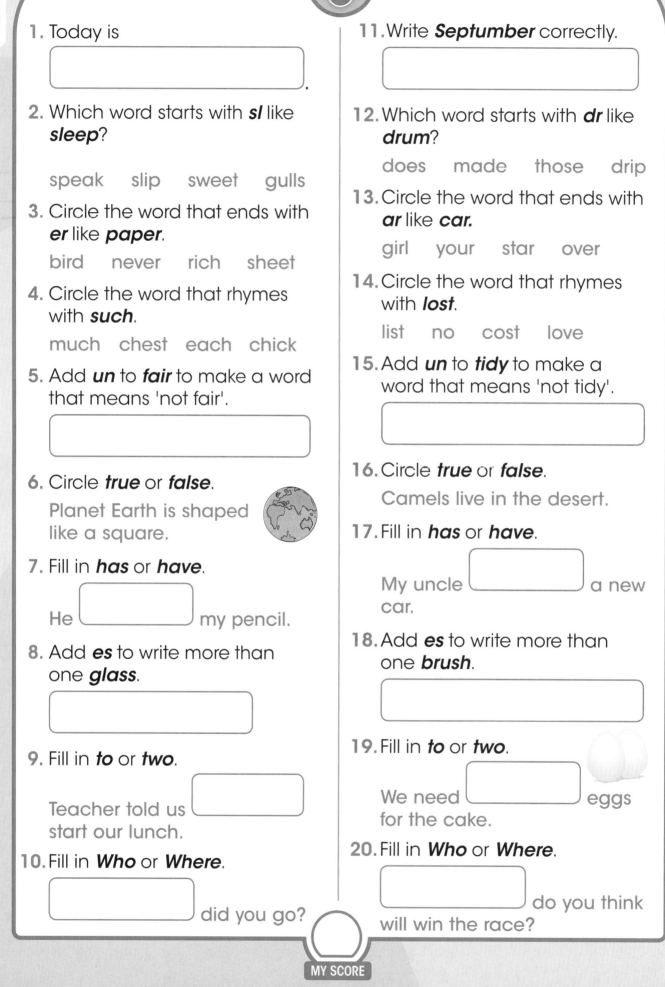

1. Today is

_____ .

2. Which word starts with **sl** like **sleep**?

   speak   slip   sweet   gulls

3. Circle the word that ends with **er** like **paper**.

   bird   never   rich   sheet

4. Circle the word that rhymes with **such**.

   much   chest   each   chick

5. Add **un** to **fair** to make a word that means 'not fair'.

6. Circle **true** or **false**.
   Planet Earth is shaped like a square.

7. Fill in **has** or **have**.

   He _____ my pencil.

8. Add **es** to write more than one **glass**.

9. Fill in **to** or **two**.

   Teacher told us _____ start our lunch.

10. Fill in **Who** or **Where**.

    _____ did you go?

11. Write **Septumber** correctly.

12. Which word starts with **dr** like **drum**?

    does   made   those   drip

13. Circle the word that ends with **ar** like **car.**

    girl   your   star   over

14. Circle the word that rhymes with **lost**.

    list   no   cost   love

15. Add **un** to **tidy** to make a word that means 'not tidy'.

16. Circle **true** or **false**.
    Camels live in the desert.

17. Fill in **has** or **have**.

    My uncle _____ a new car.

18. Add **es** to write more than one **brush**.

19. Fill in **to** or **two**.

    We need _____ eggs for the cake.

20. Fill in **Who** or **Where**.

    _____ do you think will win the race?

MY SCORE

1. Fill in **bl** or **br**.

   ____ick

2. Which word ends with **im** like **swim**, **skim**, **trim** and **him**?

   jam   slim   mime   slip

3. Write the correct word: **can** or **cane**.

   My grandad uses a _____ to walk.

4. Circle the word with **oe** in the middle like **goes** and **toes**.

   love   joey   some   come

5. Add **cake** to **pan** to make a compound word.

6. Add **ing** to **smash** to make a new word.

7. Circle the correct word.

   A wall can be made of **scones/stones**.

8. Put a dot where **and** is needed.

   He ran jumped.

9. Write the first word correctly.

   does the baby ever sleep?

10. Write **?** or **!** at the end of the sentence.

    Where is my book

11. Fill in **bl** or **br**.

    ____ank

12. Which word ends with **ub** like **tub**, **rub**, **grub** and **stub**?

    but   scrub   cube   slab

13. Write the correct word: **not** or **note**.

    Mum gave me a _____ for my teacher.

14. Circle the word with **ou** in the middle like **loud** and **foul**.

    go   school   shout   clown

15. Add **hill** to **up** to make a compound word.

16. Add **ing** to **start** to make a new word.

17. Circle the correct word.

    The boat had a flag on the **mast/mats**.

18. Put a dot where **and** is needed.

    The song was long loud.

19. Write the first word correctly.

    put the ham on the bread.

20. Write **?** or **!** at the end of the sentence.

    Mum will be very mad

MY SCORE

REVISION

1. Fill in **cl** or **cr**.

   Clue: what a king wears on his head

   _____own

2. How many syllables in **monkey**?

3. Circle the word that starts like **yes**, **yet**, **yellow** and **you.**

   Tuesday   yarn   then   they

4. Add **un** to **lucky** to make a new word that means 'not lucky'.

5. Which word do **plays**, **playing** and **played** start from?

6. Add **s** to **vet** to write more than one vet.

7. Add **es** to **switch** to mean more than one.

8. Circle the correct word.

   She has a **hoppy/happy** face.

9. Circle the word that needs a capital letter.

   Dear gran, I'm coming to visit you.

10. Write **.**, **?** or **!** at the end of the sentence.

    What is your name

11. Fill in **cl** or **cr**.

    _____ust

12. How many syllables in **father**?

13. Circle the word that starts like **photo**.

    whale   shout   phone   cheese

14. Add **un** to **zip** to make a new word that means 'to open a zip'.

15. Which word do **plants**, **planted** and **planting** start from?

16. Add **s** to **bin** to write more than one bin.

17. Add **es** to **match** to mean more than one.

18. Circle the correct word.

    The rabbit got out of his **hatch/hutch**.

19. Circle the word that needs a capital letter.

    Tell me what mum said.

20. Write **.**, **?** or **!** at the end of the sentence.

    When are we going to the shop

MY SCORE

1. Fill in **fl** or **fr**.

   ___ont

2. How many syllables in the word **rich**? ☐

3. Change **th** in **thin** to **sh** to write a new word.

4. Circle the word that rhymes with **sang**.

   song   hang   school   go

5. Add **ed** to **train** to write a new word.

6. Add **ing** to **hint** to write a new word.

7. Which is correct?

   We use/uses a hard broom.

8. Fill in **Where** or **Were**.

   ___ are they going now?

9. Write **.**, **?** or **!** at the end of the sentence.

   He is SO sorry

10. Circle the odd one out.

    paper   water   milk   tea

11. Fill in **fl** or **fr**.

    ___ick

12. How many syllables in the word **happy**? ☐

13. Change **ch** in **chick** to **th** to write a new word.

14. Circle the word that rhymes with **rain**.

    car   says   train   one

15. Add **ed** to **sail** to write a new word.

16. Add **ing** to **bring** to write a new word.

17. Which is correct?

    The tap drip/drips a lot.

18. Fill in **where** or **were**.

    The children ___ happy with the party.

19. Write **.**, **?** or **!** at the end of the sentence.

    Come back here now

20. Circle the odd one out.

    taxi   car   cabbage   bus

MY SCORE

REVISION DAYS 111–120

1. Fill in **dr** or **tr**.

   ____ess

2. How many syllables in the word **river**? ☐

3. Which word ends with **zz** like **buzz** and **fizz**?

   busy   zoom   fuzz   zebra

4. Add **bag** to **hand** to make a new word.

   ☐

5. Circle the word with **air** like **pair**.

   dairy   family   here   mouse

6. Circle the word with **ear** like **fear** that means tools or part of a machine.

   gear   house   was   some

7. Read the clue. Circle the word.

   A place where horses stay.

   library   stable   chemist

8. Read the clue then pick the **ending**.

   Clue: after first and second

   th_____   erd   ird

9. Pick **and** or **but**.

   The boy ☐ girl were yawning.

10. Write the first word correctly.

    they are good cooks.

    ☐

11. Fill in **dr** or **tr**.

    ____uck

12. How many syllables in the word **trip**? ☐

13. Which word ends with **ck** like **back** and **lick**?

    peck   cake   kitten   of

14. Add **drop** to **rain** to make a new word.

    ☐

15. Circle the word with **air** like **dairy** that means a den for a wild animal.

    where   lair   ask   once

16. Circle the word with **ear** like **gear** that means hair on the face.

    less   beard   cloud   we

17. Read the clue. Circle the word.

    A place to send letters and buy stamps.

    school   bank   post office

18. Read the clue then pick the **ending**.

    Clue: face goes red

    bl_____   osh   ush

19. Pick **and** or **but**.

    It will rain today ☐ tomorrow.

20. Write the first word correctly.

    when are we going to Gran's house? ☐

MY SCORE ◯

1. Fill in **st** or **sp**.

   ___and

2. How many syllables in **eleven**?

3. Change **ng** in **song** to **ft** to make a new word.

4. Which word starts with **dr** like **drop**?

   red   hard   drag   do

5. Add **er** to **high** to make a new word.

6. Add **est** to **rich** to make a new word.

7. Add **s** to write more than one **drum**.

8. Add **es** to write more than one **patch**.

9. Circle the **naming word**.

   The cup is heavy.

10. Unjumble the sentence.

    lost new Emma her teddy

    _____

    _____

11. Fill in **st** or **sl**.

    ___ork

12. How many syllables in **bunny**?

13. Change **ll** in **spell** to **nd** to make a new word.

14. Which word starts with **gr** like **grab**?

    crab   car   girl   green

15. Add **er** to **rich** to make a new word.

16. Add **est** to **firm** to make a new word.

17. Add **s** to write more than one **nest**.

18. Add **es** to write more than one **catch**.

19. Circle the **naming word**.

    The flower is pretty.

20. Unjumble the sentence.

    school saw friend his at Ryan

    _____

    _____

MY SCORE

REVISION

1. Fill in *pl* or *pr*.

   ____am

2. How many syllables in **dinner**? ☐

3. Circle the word with **ow** in the middle like **clown** and **frown**.

   were   work   go   brown

4. Which word starts with **ph** like **photo**?

   full   put   so   phone

5. Write the missing letters.

   Wed☐☐☐day

6. Add **un** to **even** to make a new word that means 'not level'.

   ☐

7. Circle the word with the same **ai** sound as **wait**, **train** and **paid**.

   join   afraid   tie   said

8. Unjumble the sentence.

   home Yesterday we at stayed

   _____

   _____

9. Which is correct?

   The boy **catch/catches** the ball.

   ☐

10. Circle the mistake.

    Yesterday was wednesday.

11. Fill in *pl* or *pr*.

    ____ug

12. How many syllables in **fish**? ☐

13. Circle the word with **oe** like **woes** and **goes**.

    one   note   once   tiptoe

14. Which word starts with **wh** like **where**, **what** and **when**?

    me   why   were   how

15. Write the three missing letters.

    T☐☐☐day

16. Add **un** to **cut** to make a new word that means the opposite of **cut**.

    ☐

17. Circle the word with **oi** like **oil**, **join** and **coin**.

    rain   lion   point   the

18. Unjumble the sentence.

    The cat loud the scared noise

    _____

    _____

19. Which is correct?

    Jill **fetch/fetches** a bucket of water.

    ☐

20. Circle the mistake.

    I eat fish on friday.

MY SCORE

1. Fill in **sm** or **sn**.

   ___ell

2. How many syllables in **notch**?

3. Change **oi** in **soil** to **ea** to write a new word.

4. Add **er** to **loud** to make a new word.

5. Add **est** to **faint** to make a new word.

6. Circle the word with **are** like **dare**.

   read   friend   fare   of

7. Draw a line under the **naming word**.

   He got a new kitten.

8. Circle the correct spelling.

   wold   woold   would

9. Another word for **fix** is:

   watch   mend

   paint   cook

10. Write **.**, **?** or **!** at the end of the sentence.

    Your tree has some fruit on it

11. Fill in **sm** or **sn**.

    ___ore

12. How many syllables in **hutch**?

13. Change **ou** in **shout** to **or** to write a new word.

14. Add **er** to **faint** to make a new word.

15. Add **est** to **fair** to make a new word.

16. Circle the word with **are** like **fare**.

    wear   car   were   bare

17. Draw a line under the **naming word**.

    She drew a great picture.

18. Circle the correct spelling.

    befoor   before   befour

19. Another word for **shouted** is:

    laughed   roared

    noticed   listened

20. Write **.**, **?** or **!** at the end of the sentence.

    There are a lot of clouds today

MY SCORE